Exploring maths

Home Book

4

PEARSON Longman

Anita Straker, Tony Fisher, Rosalyn Hyde, Sue Jennings and Jonathan Longstaffe

Published by Pearson Education Limited, Edinburgh Gate, Harlow, Essex, CM20 2JE, England
www.longman.co.uk

First published 2008
ISBN-13 978-1-405-84416-1
Cover illustration by M.C. Escher

Typeset by Tech-Set, Gateshead

Printed and bound in Great Britian at Scotprint, Haddington

The publisher's policy is to use paper manufactured from sustainable forests.

Picture Credits
The publisher would like to thank the following for their kind permission to reproduce their photographs:

(Key: b-bottom; c-centre; l-left; r-right; t-top)

Alamy Images: Adrian Sherratt 53; Blend Images 133b; Bubbles Photolibrary 61; Chris Howes/Wild Places Photography 44; Colin Underhill 101; Corbis Premium RF 137; David Pearson 90; Geoff du Feu 133t; Imagestate 87; Mediacolor's 93; Mike Hill 51; Photofusion Picture Library 55; Vario Images GmbH & Co. KG 104; **Art Directors and TRIP photo Library:** Helene Rogers 112; **Bridgeman Art Library Ltd:** Private Collection, The Stapleton Collection 71tr; Victoria & Albert Museum, London, UK 71tl; **Corbis:** Bettmann 10; **DK Images:** 71tc; Dave King 67; Geoff Dann(c)DK courtesy of Chateau de Sully, Sully sur Loire, France 73; Library of Congress 21b; Matthew Ward 46t; Philip Enticknap 8l, 8r; Steve Gorton 99, 113; **Getty Images:** Richard Harrington/Hulton Archive 21t; **iStockphoto:** 14, 17, 24, 25, 35, 41, 46b, 49, 64, 110, 115; **Jupiter Unlimited:** 29, 29 (ace), 29 (four), 29 (three), 29 (two); **Pearson Education Ltd:** 1, 126l, 126r; **Photofusion Picture Library:** David Montford 121; **Anita Straker:** 111

Front Cover: The M.C Escher Company-Holland: M.C Escher's Symmetry Drawing E55(c)27 The M.C Escher Company-Holland. All rights reserved. www.mcescher.com

All other images © Pearson Education

Picture Research by: Louise Edgeworth

Every effort has been made to trace the copyright holders and we apologise in advance for any unintentional omissions. We would be pleased to insert the appropriate acknowledgement in any subsequent edition of this publication.

Contents

Properties of numbers

TASK 1: Order of operations

 Points to remember

- Deal with brackets first.
- When there are no brackets, multiply and divide before you add and subtract.
  Example: $2 \times (3 + 4) = 2 \times 7 = 14$

1 Each ● represents a missing operation ($+$, $-$, $\times$ or $\div$).
Copy and complete these equations. Use your calculator to help you.

a $(56 \bullet 38) \bullet 62 = 1116$ b $(2030 \bullet 35) \bullet 97 = 155$

c $650 \bullet (48 \bullet 35) = 50$ d $27 \bullet (13 \bullet 15) = 5265$

TASK 2: Adding and subtracting directed numbers

 Did you know that...?

The place that you most often find positive and negative numbers is on thermometers that measure air temperature.

 Points to remember

- When you are adding or subtracting positive and negative numbers, two signs together can be regarded as one sign:

  $+ +$ is $+$ $+ -$ is $-$ $- +$ is $-$ $- -$ is $+$

  Two signs that are the same are equivalent to $+$.
  Two signs that are different are equivalent to $-$.

1 Find the missing numbers. Copy and complete these.

a $2 + (-6) = \square$	**b** $4 - (-1) = \square$	**c** $(-4) + (-5) = \square$
d $2 - \square = 7$	**e** $9 - \square = 3$	**f** $(-4) + \square = -6$
g $\square + (-7) = 0$	**h** $2 + \square = -6$	**i** $3 - \square = 8$

TASK 3: Multiplying and dividing directed numbers

 **Points to remember**

⊙ Multiplication or division of numbers where the two signs are the same results in +.
Multiplication where the two signs are different results in −.

1 Find the missing numbers. Copy and complete these.

a $2 \times (-6) = \square$	**b** $4 \div (-1) = \square$	**c** $(-4) \times (-5) = \square$
d $14 \div \square = -2$	**e** $(-9) \times \square = 36$	**f** $\square \times (-1) = -3$
g $(-4) \times \square = -24$	**h** $\square \div (-7) = 0$	**i** $2 \times \square = -6$
j $\square \div (-5) = -2$	**k** $3 \times \square = 21$	**l** $\square \div (-3) = 9$

TASK 4: Powers and roots

 Points to remember

⊙ The **square** of a number n is n^2 or $n \times n$.
Example: $9^2 = 9 \times 9 = 81$, $(-9)^2 = -9 \times -9 = 81$

⊙ $\sqrt{n}$ is the **square root** of n. Example: $\sqrt{81} = \pm 9$

⊙ You can find the value of 5^2 by pressing these calculator keys: ⑤ $\boxed{x^2}$.

⊙ You usually find the square root of 81 by pressing these calculator keys: ⑧ ① $\boxed{\sqrt{}}$.
On some calculators you press the square root key first like this:
$\boxed{\sqrt{}}$ ⑧ ①.

(1) Any positive whole number can be written as the sum of four square numbers, e.g.

$$23 = 1^2 + 2^2 + 3^2 + 3^2$$

Investigate different ways of writing 150 as the sum of four square numbers.
How many different ways are there?
The same numbers in a different order does not count as different.

(2) Now find a way of writing 150 as the sum of three square numbers.

TASK 5: Multiples, factors and primes

⦿ Points to remember

⊙ Writing a number as the product of its prime factors is called the **prime factor decomposition** of the number.

Example: $24 = 2 \times 2 \times 2 \times 3$ or $2^3 \times 3$.

⊙ To find the **highest common factor (HCF)** of two numbers, find the product of all the prime factors common to both numbers.

Example: 8 has prime factors $2 \times 2 \times 2$ and 12 has prime factors $2 \times 2 \times 3$. The highest common factor is 2×2.

⊙ To find the **lowest common multiple (LCM)** of two numbers, find the smallest number that is a multiple of each of the numbers.

Example: 8 has prime factors $2 \times 2 \times 2$ and 12 has prime factors $2 \times 2 \times 3$. The lowest common multiple of 8 and 12 is $2 \times 2 \times 2 \times 3 = 48$.

(1) Use a division method to find the prime factors of:

   a 84   b 175

(2) Use a tree method to find the prime factors of:

   a 400   b 396

(3) Use prime factors to work out the HCF and LCM of:

   a 100 and 150   b 78 and 91

(4) The three missing numbers are different prime numbers greater than 3.

$$\square \times \square \times \square = 1001$$

What are the three prime numbers?

Angles and shapes

TASK 1: Corresponding angles

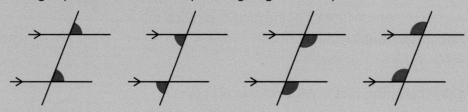

Points to remember

⊙ The marked angles are called **corresponding angles**.

⊙ Corresponding angles are formed when a transversal cuts a pair of straight parallel lines. Corresponding angles are equal.

⊙ When you calculate angles, always include your reasons.

① In each of these diagrams, a pair of parallel straight lines is cut by a transversal.

Calculate the size of each angle marked by a letter.
Give a reason for each answer.

a

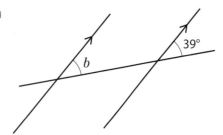

b

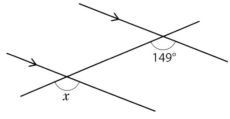

c

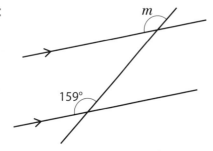

d

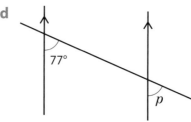

(2) In this diagram, a pair of parallel straight lines is cut by two transversals.

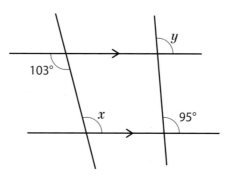

Calculate the size of each angle marked by a letter.
Give a reason for each answer.
You can use vertically opposite angles and corresponding angles.
You may have to find some extra angles.

(3) In these diagrams, two or more parallel straight lines are cut by transversals or other parallel lines.

Calculate the size of each angle marked by a letter.

You may have to find some other angles before you can find the marked angle.

a

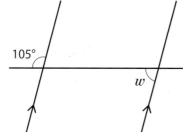

b

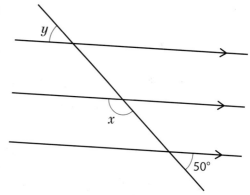

c

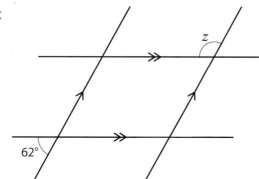

TASK 2: Alternate angles

Points to remember

⊙ The marked angles are called **alternate angles**.

⊙ Alternate angles are formed when a transversal cuts a pair of parallel straight lines. Alternate angles are equal.

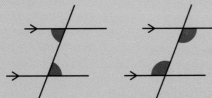 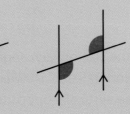

⊙ When you calculate angles, always include your reasons.

⊙ You may need to work out other angles along the way.

⊙ Draw diagrams neatly.

① In each diagram, a pair of parallel straight lines is cut by one or two transversals.

Find the size of each angle marked by a letter.
Remember to include your reasons.

a

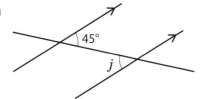

b

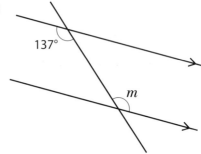

c

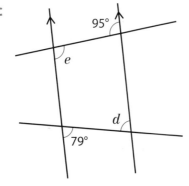

d

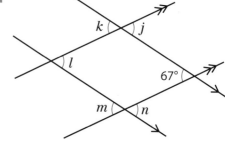

(2) This diagram shows a pair of parallel straight lines cut by two intersecting transversals.

Find the sizes of each angle marked by a letter.
Remember to include your reasons.

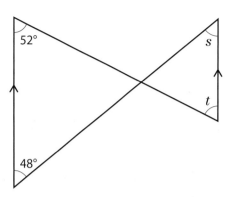

TASK 3: Angles in a triangle and a quadrilateral

Points to remember

⊙ A **proof** is a sequence of steps or statements that follow on logically, one after another, to show that something is true.

⊙ A proof uses the information that is given, or that you can work out from this information.

⊙ In a proof, you may need to join points in a diagram or to construct a line.

(1) Here is an isosceles triangle.

Calculate the size of angle x.

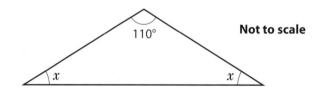

Not to scale

(2) *2005 level 5*

The diagram shows triangle PQR.

Work out the sizes of angles a, b and c.

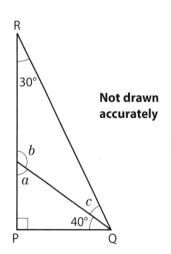

Not drawn accurately

3 Shape WXYZ is a rectangle. XZ is parallel to UV.

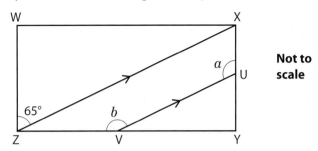

Not to scale

Calculate the size of angles a and b.

TASK 4: Understanding congruence

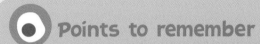

Points to remember

- **Congruent shapes** are exactly the same size and shape.
- In congruent shapes, corresponding angles are equal and corresponding sides are equal.

Examples

An exact copy of a photograph is congruent to the original.

These two triangles are exactly the same shape and size.

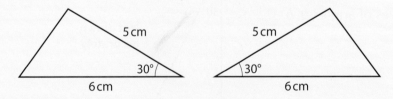

congruent triangles

This is true because it is only possible to draw one triangle with these dimensions. The lengths of the two lines are fixed and the angle between them is fixed.

You will need some squared dotty paper.

1 Look at these shapes. Write down the pairs that are congruent.

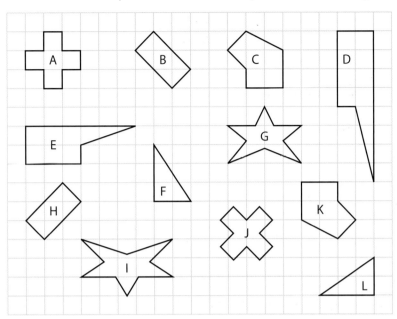

2 a Use squared dotty paper.

How many triangles congruent to this triangle can you draw
on a 3 by 3 grid?
The triangles can be rotated, reflected or translated.

b Use squared dotty paper.

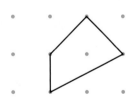

How many quadrilaterals congruent to this quadrilateral can
you draw on a 4 by 4 grid?

TASK 5: Properties of quadrilaterals

Points to remember

⊙ Rectangles, squares, parallelograms, rhombuses, kites and arrowheads are made up from pairs of congruent triangles.

① Draw a parallelogram.
Mark on your drawing all the sides that are equal in length and all the angles that are equal.

② A square is made up from two congruent triangles.
Draw one of the triangles and mark on it the sizes of the angles.

③ Investigate the shapes you can make from a pair of congruent right-angled isosceles triangles.
Draw the shapes, showing both triangles.
Mark on your drawings the equal angles and the equal sides.
Write the name of the shape under each drawing.

TASK 6: Solving geometrical problems

Did you know that...?

Euclid's *Elements of Geometry* were the first mathematics books to be printed. They were translated into many different languages and became the standard textbooks on geometry for centuries.

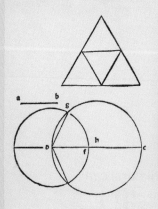

Page from a Latin translation of Euclid's *Elements of Geometry*

1   AB and CD are parallel straight lines.
    Transversal EF cuts AB and CD at I and J respectively so that angle AIJ is 86°.
    A line GH, parallel to EF, cuts AB and CD at points L and K respectively.
    A straight line joins points J and L so that angle JLK is 47°.

    Find angles IJL, JKL, KJL and ILJ.

    What sort of triangle is triangle LIJ? Explain why.

    What sort of triangle is triangle JKL? Explain why.

    What shape is IJKL? Explain why.

TASK 1: Term-to-term rules

● Points to remember

⊙ A **sequence** of numbers follows a rule.

⊙ You can work out the next term in a sequence if you know the **term-to-term rule**.

Example: 3, 7, 11, 15, …
The term-to-term rule for this sequence is 'add 4'.
The next term is 19.

(1) Write the term-to-term rule and the next five terms for each of these sequences.

a 5, 14, 23, 32, …　　　　　b 28, 26, 24, 22, …

c 13, 21, 29, 37, …　　　　　d 2, 4, 8, 16, …

e 0.5, 2, 3.5, 5, …　　　　　f 10, 9.7, 9.4, 9.1, …

g 1, 3, 9, 27, …　　　　　　h 200, 100, 50, 25, …

(2) Write down the first five terms of each of these sequences.

	1st term	Term-to-term rule
a	1	add 8
b	500	subtract 22
c	0	add 33
d	0.6	subtract 0.1
e	10	subtract 10
f	1	multiply by 2 and add 3
g	3	multiply by 5 and add 1
h	5	multiply by 2 and subtract 3

TASK 2: Position-to-term rules

Points to remember

- You can work out any term in a sequence if you know the formula for the *n*th term.

- The difference between consecutive terms will help you to find the *n*th term.

Example: 5, 9, 13, 17, …, $4n + 1$

The 20th term of this sequence is $4 \times 20 + 1 = 81$.

1 Use the formula for the *n*th term to generate the next four terms of each number sequence.

	nth term	**Sequence**
a	$5n$	5, 10, …
b	$5n + 4$	9, 14, …
c	$5n - 2$	3, 8, …
d	$3n + 7$	10, 13, …
e	$9n - 5$	4, 13, …
f	$2n - 0.5$	1.5, 3.5, …
g	$0.5n + 6$	6.5, 7, …

2 Use the formula for the *n*th term of a sequence to work out the given term.

	nth term	**Find this term**
a	$3n + 11$	20th term
b	$2n + 7$	36th term
c	$4n - 9$	14th term
d	$5n + 25$	50th term
e	$11n - 13$	17th term
f	$4n - 23$	99th term
g	$7n + 6$	365th term

3 Find the formula for the *n*th term for each of these sequences.

a 4, 7, 10, 13, … b 7, 9, 11, 13, 15, …

c 2, 8, 14, 20, … d 9, 19, 29, 39, …

e 1, 6, 11, 16, … f 2, 2.5, 3, 3.5, …

TASK 3: Using a spreadsheet to generate sequences

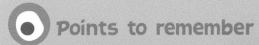

Points to remember

- You can use a spreadsheet to explore sequences.

- Each cell in a spreadsheet is given a name using the column heading and the row heading. For example, the first cell is called A1.

1 This sequence has been generated using a spreadsheet on a computer.

   a What formula do you need to enter in A3 to generate the sequence using a term-to-term rule?

   b In which cell will the 50th term be?

	A
1	Sequence of numbers
2	20
3	24
4	28
5	32
6	36
7	40
8	44
9	48
10	52
11	56
12	

2 This sequence has been generated using a spreadsheet on a computer.

   a What formula do you need to enter in A3 to generate the position numbers?

   b What formula do you need to enter in B2 to generate the sequence using a position-to-term rule?

   c In which cell will the 100th term be?

	A	B	C
1	Position	Term	Difference
2	1	7	
3	2	10	
4	3	13	
5	4	16	
6	5	19	
7	6	22	
8	7	25	
9	8	28	
10	9	31	
11	10	34	
12	11	37	
13	12	40	
14	...	...	
15	n	?	

TASK 4: Exploring patterns

①   Patterns like these are made with regular octagons.

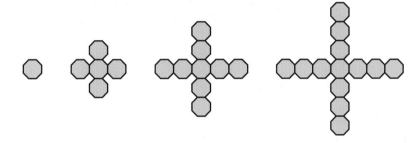

    a How many octagons are needed for the 5th pattern?

    b The pattern continues in the same way.
       Draw what you think might be the 5th pattern.

    c Work out a formula for the number of octagons needed for the nth pattern.

②   Investigate other patterns with octagons.
    Work out the formula for the number of octagons needed for the nth pattern.

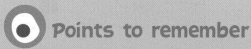

Whole numbers, decimals and fractions

TASK 1: Place value

> ### Points to remember
>
> - $0.3 = \frac{3}{10}$ $0.09 = \frac{9}{100}$ $0.004 = \frac{4}{1000}$
> - When you round decimals, look at the first unwanted digit.
>   If it is 5, 6, 7, 8 or 9, add 1 to the last digit that you keep.
>   Then leave off all the unwanted digits.
> - Round up 'halfway' numbers.
>   Examples: 42.5 rounds up to 43; 8750 rounds up to 8800.
> - 7.96 rounded to one decimal place is 8.0, not 8.

1   Copy and complete the table.

Round:	to the nearest 10	to the nearest whole number	to one decimal place	to two decimal places
53.292				
8.851				
159.444				
43.0999				

2   An electric kettle holds 1.8 litres of water.
It is filled 12 times a day.
Approximately how much water is used to fill the kettle each month?
Show how you worked out your answer.

3 The mass of one small cake is 38.6 g.
4 cakes are packed in 1 box.
24 boxes are packed in 1 crate.
38 crates are stacked in 1 van.
Estimate the total mass of the small
cakes in the van.
Show how you worked out your answer.

TASK 2: Ordering, adding and subtracting decimals

 Points to remember

⊙ When you compare two decimals, compare the sizes of digits in
equivalent places.

⊙ For column addition and subtraction of decimals:

– line up the decimal points, writing tenths under tenths, hundredths
under hundredths, and so on;

– if you wish, fill gaps at the end of the decimal places with zeros;

– show 'carry' figures clearly;

– change units (e.g. pounds and pence, centimetres and metres) to the
same unit.

1 This table shows metric conversions.

1 cm = 10 mm	$1 \text{ cm}^2 = 100 \text{ mm}^2$
1 m = 100 cm	$1 \text{ m}^2 = 10\,000 \text{ cm}^2$
1 km = 1000 m	$1 \text{ km}^2 = 1\,000\,000 \text{ m}^2$

Use the information to convert each of these measurements.

a 0.45 km into mm   b 1950 cm^2 into m^2

c 32 500 mm into km   d 0.0065 km^2 into cm^2

Now change:

e 3.6 kg into g   f 17 250 ml into litres

(2) Without using a calculator, work out the answers to these calculations.
Then place the answers in order from the smallest to the largest to spell something you might like to own.

O $6.06 + 0.293$ E $7 - 0.036$ I $54 \div 8$ G 2.024×3

D $5.01 + 1.39$ M 1.68×4 L $25.42 \div 4$ N $8.054 - 1.1$

(3) Jack did an experiment 20 times to measure his reaction time.
Here are his times in seconds.

0.26 0.31 0.40 0.26 0.31 0.41 0.27 0.31 0.19 0.28 0.33
0.23 0.30 0.36 0.26 0.31 0.38 0.27 0.32 0.40

Find Jack's median time.

TASK 3: Multiplication and division calculations

Points to remember

⊙ When you multiply two or more numbers together you get their **product**.

Example: The product of 5, 6 and 7 is $5 \times 6 \times 7 = 210$.

(1) Try this investigation.

The number 12 can be split into whole-number parts in lots of different ways, e.g.

$12 = 11 + 1$
$12 = 3 + 2 + 7$
$12 = 1 + 2 + 9$

Multiply the parts together to form a product, e.g.

$11 \times 1 = 11$
$3 \times 2 \times 7 = 42$
$1 \times 2 \times 9 = 18$

Investigate ways of splitting 12 into whole-number parts.

a Make a product of 32.

b Make 32 by splitting 12 in a different way.

c Make a product of 40.

d Make 40 by splitting 12 in a different way.

e What is the biggest product you can make by splitting 12 into whole-number parts?

Now start splitting the number 13 into whole-number parts.

f What is the biggest product that you can make?

TASK 4: Using a calculator

 Points to remember

When you use a calculator:

⊙ estimate the result of a calculation;

⊙ use the CLEAR-ALL key before each new calculation;

⊙ use the CLEAR key to clear the last entry;

⊙ use the memory to store answers to parts of a calculation or to keep a total;

⊙ think carefully about the meaning of the numbers in the final display;

⊙ round the answer to a sensible number, depending on the context;

⊙ check the answer against the estimate.

1 What is the total cost of these items?

> 2 tins of tuna at £1.16 per tin
> 4 large onions at 23p each
> 250 g mushrooms at £2.20 per kilogram
> 3 tins of coconut milk at 89p each
> 2 packets of rice at £1.69 per packet
> 1 tub of curry powder at £1.15

2 Each ● represents a missing operation (+, −, × or ÷).
Copy and complete these calculations. Use your calculator to help you.

a (37 ● 21) ● 223 = 1000

b (756 ● 18) ● 29 = 1218

c 27 ● (36 ● 18) = 675

d 31 ● (87 ● 19) = 2108

TASK 5: Equivalent fractions and fractions of quantities

● Points to remember

- ⊙ To convert a fraction into an equivalent fraction, multiply or divide the numerator and the denominator by the same number.

- ⊙ You can use your calculator to find equivalent fractions.

  The fraction key often looks like a^b/c.

  Enter 4 a^b/c 6. The display represents the fraction $\frac{4}{6}$ and will look something like:

  > ⎡ 4⌐6 ⎤

  If you now press = the fraction will be simplified to $\frac{2}{3}$.

- ⊙ Find a fraction of a number by using multiplication and division.
  Example: Find $\frac{5}{8}$ of 27.

  $27 \div 8 = 3.375$ divide 27 by 8

  $3.375 \times 5 = 16.875$ then multiply by 5

One full turn is 360°.

This sector of the circle contains an angle of 100°.

This sector is $\frac{100}{360} = \frac{5}{18}$ of the whole circle.

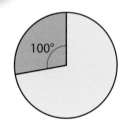

1 What fraction of a whole circle is a sector containing an angle of:

a 80°

b 300°

c 135°

d 17°

2 These fractions refer to sectors of circles. What angle does each sector contain?

a $\frac{5}{8}$

b $\frac{2}{9}$

c $\frac{13}{18}$

d $\frac{19}{30}$

3 Write the answers to these calculations. You may use a calculator.

a $\frac{5}{8}$ of 2 hours

b $\frac{7}{12}$ of £303

c $\frac{3}{4}$ of 21 kg

d $\frac{4}{5}$ of 32 cm

e $\frac{5}{8}$ of 300 m²

f $\frac{8}{25}$ of 65 litres

TASK 6: Calculations with fractions

Points to remember

⊙ Given a fractional part, find the whole by using division then multiplication.

Example: Four fifths of a bottle of water is 300 ml.
How much water is there in a full bottle?

Four fifths is 300 ml.
One fifth is $300 \div 4 = 75$ ml.
Five fifths is $75 \times 5 = 375$ ml.

⊙ Add or subtract simple fractions like this.

$\frac{5}{8} + \frac{7}{12} = \frac{15}{24} + \frac{14}{24}$ Change the fractions to a common denominator.

$= \frac{29}{24}$ Add the fractions.

$= 1\frac{5}{24}$ Change the improper fraction to a mixed number.

$\frac{11}{12} - \frac{3}{4} = \frac{11}{12} - \frac{9}{12}$ Change the fractions to a common denominator.

$= \frac{2}{12}$ Subtract the fractions.

$= \frac{1}{6}$ Simplify the fraction by cancelling.

1   Pirate Pete found some rubies in a tin.

He gave one third of his rubies to his mate
and one fifth to the bosun.
He kept the other 28 rubies.

How many rubies did the bosun get?

2   24 pirates landed on a treasure island.

One third of them found some gold coins.
One quarter of them found some rubies.
One half of them found neither.

How many of them found both gold
coins and rubies?

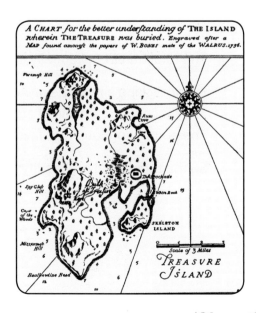

Probability

TASK 1: Theoretical probability

 Points to remember

⊙ Probabilities range from 0 (impossible) to 1 (certain).
  They are written as fractions, decimals or percentages.

⊙ An event can have different **outcomes**.

⊙ **Equally likely outcomes** occur in fair trials.
  Outcomes are not equally likely when trials are biased.

⊙ If the outcomes are equally likely, the **theoretical probability** of a
  particular event is:

$$\frac{\text{number of favourable outcomes}}{\text{total number of possible outcomes}}$$

Example

Trial: One of the first twenty multiples of 5 is picked at random.

Possible outcomes: 5 10 15 20 25 30 35 40 45   50
                   55 60 65 70 75 80 85 90 95 100

The total number of equally likely outcomes is 20.

Event: Picking a multiple of 3
The outcomes in the event are: 15 30 45 60 75 90
The number of outcomes favourable to this event is 6.

So the theoretical probability of picking a multiple of 3 is $\frac{6}{20} = \frac{3}{10}$.

1 One of these number cards is picked at random.

| 1 | 3 | 1 | 5 | 2 | 4 | 4 | 1 | 6 | 6 |

   a Write down the theoretical probability of picking a card numbered:
     i 1   **ii** 5   **iii** 2 or 3   **iv** 1, 2 or 3

   b Write down the theoretical probability of picking:
     i a prime number   **ii** a square number
     iii a multiple of 3   **iv** a factor of 6

Three in a line: rules

Draw a 4 by 4 grid.
Take turns to place a red or a blue counter on the grid.

To place a counter on the grid:

⊙ Choose box 1, box 2 or box 3 at random.
  The boxes contain different numbers of red and blue counters.

 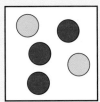 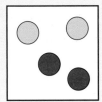

     Box 1   **Box 2**   **Box 3**

⊙ Pick a counter at random from the box and put it on the grid.
  This means that you might have to put your opponent's colour on the grid.

The winner is the first to have three of their own colour in a horizontal, vertical or diagonal line.

---

2 In this game Chloe is playing red. It is Chloe's turn.

   a Chloe is hoping she picks box 2. Explain why.

   b If Chloe picks a red, where should she put it? Explain why.

   c If Chloe picks a blue, where should she put it? Explain why.

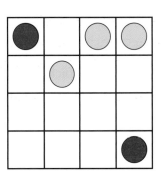

TASK 2: Events not happening

 Points to remember

⊙ The probability of an event not happening is
1 minus the probability of the event happening.

Example

A letter from the word PROBABLE is picked at random.

There are 8 equally likely outcomes.

In the event 'picking a vowel', there are 3 outcomes : O, A and E.
In the event 'not picking a vowel', there are 5 outcomes : P, R, B, B and L.

The theoretical probability of picking a vowel is $\frac{3}{8}$.
The theoretical probability of not picking a vowel is $\frac{5}{8}$.

The probability of not picking a vowel is
1 minus the probability of picking a vowel.

---

① A letter from the word CHANCE is picked at random.
What is the probability that the letter is:

   a the letter C?   **b** not the letter C?

   c a consonant?   **d** not a consonant?

   e in the word PROBABLE?   **f** not in the word PROBABLE?

② In a set of snooker balls, there are
15 red balls and 1 ball each of
yellow, green, brown, blue, pink,
black and white.

A set of snooker balls is put in a bag
and one is picked at random.

What is the probability that the
ball is:

   a red?   **b** not red?

   c pink?   **d** not pink?

   e red or white?   **f** not red or white?

TASK 3: The probability of two events

Points to remember

⊙ When two events occur at the same time or one after the other, you can use a list or table to record the equally likely outcomes.

⊙ Use the list or table to work out the probability from:

$$\frac{\text{number of favourable outcomes}}{\text{total number of possible outcomes}}$$

Example

This table shows all the equally likely outcomes when two fair coins are tossed.

		1st throw	
		H	T
2nd throw	H	HH	TH
	T	HT	TT

There are 4 equally likely outcomes.
The probability of each of them is $\frac{1}{4}$.

In a pack of playing cards there are four suits:
clubs (**C**), diamonds (**D**), hearts (**H**) and spades (**S**).

Bill shuffles a pack of playing cards.
He turns over the top card and records whether it is
a club (**C**), diamond (**D**), heart (**H**) or spade (**S**).
Joan repeats this with a different pack of cards.

① Copy and complete this table to show all the possible outcomes.

		Bill's card			
		C	D	H	S
Joan's card	C				
	D				
	H				
	S				

(2) Use the table to work out the probability that the two cards:

    a include at least one club;

    b have the same suit;

    c are red;

    d are two black cards of a different suit.

TASK 4: Experimental probability

 Points to remember

- The **experimental probability** of an event is:

$$\frac{\text{number of successful trials}}{\text{total number of trials}}$$

- Different experiments can give different values of experimental probability.

- Experimental probability gives a better estimate of probability as the number of trials increases.

Example

James sticks a piece of Blu-Tack on one side of a coin and throws it 10 times. He gets these results.

  H H T H T H T H H H

The number of heads is 7; the total number of trials is 10.
So the experimental probability of a head is $\frac{7}{10} = 0.7$.

Anna throws the same coin 100 times. Here are her results.

Outcome	Frequency
H	64
T	36

The experimental probability of a head is $\frac{64}{100} = 0.64$.

Anna's experiment gives a more reliable estimate of probability because of the greater number of throws.

1 a Emily spins the arrow on this spinner 20 times.
      Here are her results.

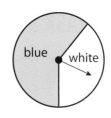

B   B   B   B   B   W   W   B   W   B
B   B   W   B   B   B   B   B   B   B

Work out the experimental probability that the
arrow lands on blue.

b Tom spins the arrow on the same spinner 50 times. Here are his results.

B   W   W   B   W   B   B   B   W   B
W   W   B   W   B   W   W   W   B   W
B   B   B   W   W   W   W   B   B   W
B   W   B   B   B   B   B   B   B   B
B   W   W   B   B   W   W   B   B   B

Work out the experimental probability that the arrow lands on blue.

c Whose experiment gives a more reliable estimate of the probability of the arrow
   landing on blue?
   Give a reason for your answer.

2 Abdullah and Charlotte throw a dart at a target.
   They either hit the centre (H) or miss the centre (M).

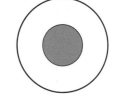

a Abdullah records the result of his throws like this.

H   M   H   M   H   H   H   M   H   H   H   H   M
H   M   H   M   H   M   M   H   H   H   M   M

What is the experimental probability of Abdullah hitting the centre?
Give your answer as a percentage.

b Charlotte summarises the result of her throws like this.

Outcome	Frequency
H	86
M	114

What is the experimental probability of Charlotte hitting the centre?
Give your answer as a decimal.

TASK 5: Are you lucky?

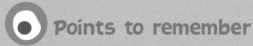

⬤ Points to remember

⊙ Some games involve chance. Some involve skill. Some involve a mixture of both.

⊙ Using ideas of probability can give you the best chance of winning a game.

(1) Daniel and Anna play a game with two dice. They roll the dice and multiply the two numbers to get a score. In the picture the score is $6 \times 3 = 18$.

For each roll:

⊙ Daniel gets a point if the score is even;

⊙ Anna gets a point if the score is odd.

The first player to get 10 points wins the game.

Who should win the game, Daniel or Anna? Use a table to explain your answer.

How would you change the rules to make the game fair?

(2) Jessica and Ben play a game using this spinner. They spin the arrow many times.

If it stops on an odd number, Jessica gets 2 points.

If it stops on an even number, Ben gets 3 points.

Is this a fair game? Write **Yes** or **No**. Explain your answer.

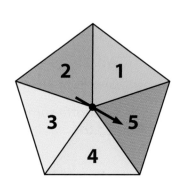

TASK 6: Theory and experiment

 Points to remember

⊙ When a probability experiment is repeated, the results may be different.

⊙ If a trial is fair, and the number of trials is large, the experimental probability is close to the theoretical probability.

Make some number cards by writing the numbers 1, 2, 3, 4 and 5 on one side of five identical pieces of paper. If you prefer you could use cards from a pack of playing cards.

1 One of the cards is picked at random.
What is the theoretical probability of picking an odd number?

2 Put the cards face down on a table so that you can't see the numbers.
Shuffle them around.
Pick one of the cards at random (or ask a friend to pick one).
Record whether it is odd or even.
Repeat this trial 50 times.
Work out the experimental probability of picking an odd number after every 10 trials.
Record the results in a table like this. Write the experimental probabilities as a decimal.

Number of trials	10	20	30	40	50
Experimental probability					

3 Compare the experimental probabilities of picking an odd number with the theoretical probability of picking an odd number.
What do you notice?

A 4.2 Expressions and formulae

TASK 1: Simplifying expressions

Points to remember

- **Like terms** have the same combination of letters.
- Simplify an expression by collecting together like terms.
- Use a grid to help multiply out a bracket.
  For example, work out $3(2x + 5)$ like this.

$\times$	$2x + 5$
3	$6x + 15$

1 Simplify these expressions by collecting together like terms.

    a $3x + 5x + 3y + 7y$ b $8 + 5p + 7q + 9 + 3p$

    c $4n - 3 + 5n - 8$ d $6x - 3y - 5x + 3y$

    e $5y + 14 - 8x - 2y + 13x$ f $7n + 35 + 9n - 27 + 19m$

2 Multiply out the brackets in these expressions.

    a $3(x + 5)$ b $7(y + 8)$

    c $9(x - 2)$ d $2(4x - 3)$

    e $5(3x - 9)$ f $10(7x + 6)$

3 Multiply out the brackets and simplify these expressions.

    a $3(2x + 9) + 5(3x + 1)$ b $4(5x + 1) + 6(4x + 7)$

    c $9(8x + 1) + 7(9x - 2)$ d $5(5x - 4) + 10(9x + 3)$

    e $12(2x - 3) + 5(7x - 9)$ f $2(13x + 4) + 7(6x - 5)$

TASK 2: Using formulae

Points to remember

⊙ A **formula** is shorthand for a general rule.

For example, the formula for the area of a rectangle is lw, where l is the length and w the width.

Substitute values for l and w to work out the area.

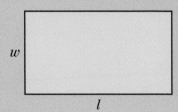

① Find the value of the formulae using the values given.

a $2xy$ $x = 3, y = 5$

b $5pqr$ $p = 4, q = 7, r = 2$

c $3x + 2y$ $x = 9, y = 6$

d $2(s + t)$ $s = 12, t = 9$

e $5(3m + 4n)$ $m = 8, n = 1$

f $6(5a - 2b)$ $a = 4, b = 7$

g $8(7p + 3q - r)$ $p = 2, q = 7, r = 10$

② The area of a trapezium is $\frac{1}{2}(a + b)h$, where a and b are the lengths of the parallel sides and h is the perpendicular distance between them measured in centimetres.

a Work out the area of the trapezium in cm^3 when $a = 4$, $b = 7$ and $h = 6$.

b The area of a trapezium is 47.5 cm^2, and $a = 10$ and $b = 9$. Find h.

③ The nth term of a sequence is $5(2n + 3)$.

a Work out the 100th term of the sequence.

b What term is the number 265?

TASK 3: Simplifying expressions with powers

 Points to remember

- **Index notation** is used as shorthand when numbers are multiplied by themselves.
  $$3 \times 3 \times 3 \times 3 \times 3 \times 3 = 3^6$$

- The same notation is used in algebra when letters are multiplied by themselves.
  $$a \times a \times a \times a \times a \times a = a^6$$
  We say 'a raised to the power of six'.

- $5x^2y^3$ means $5 \times x \times x \times y \times y \times y$.
  When $x = 2$ and $y = 3$,
  $$5x^2y^3 = 5 \times 2 \times 2 \times 3 \times 3 \times 3 = 540.$$

1 Write these algebraic terms in index form.

a $n \times n \times n \times n$

b $p \times p \times p$

c $3 \times x \times x \times x \times x$

d $5 \times x \times x \times y \times y \times y$

2 Work out the value of the terms.

a x^3y^2 $x = 2, y = 5$

b p^4q $p = 3, q = 1$

c $5s^2t^5$ $s = 4, t = 2$

d $7pq^2r$ $p = 10, q = 4, r = 12$

e $8x^2y^2$ $x = 6, y = 9$

f $7m^2n^4$ $m = 7, n = 3$

g $10wx^2y$ $w = 0.5, x = 5, y = 2$

h $4pq^3r^2$ $p = 4, q = 3, r = 10$

3 These are the nth terms of number sequences. Find the term specified.

a $n(n + 6)$ 8th term

b $n(n - 1)$ 50th term

c $2n^2 + 3$ 6th term

d $3n^3$ 9th term

TASK 4: Using algebraic expressions

◉ Points to remember

⊙ A **formula** is an algebraic expression in which the letters represent something in real life.
For example, the formula for the area of a square is x^2, where x is the length of each side of the square.

(1)

a The area of a square lid of a box is x^2, where x is the length of the side of the square measured in centimetres. What is the area when the side of the lid is 15 cm long?

b The volume of a box in the shape of a cube is x^3, where x is the length of a side of the cube measured in centimetres. What is the volume when the side of the box is 4 cm?

c The surface area of a box in the shape of a cube is $6x^2$, where x is the length of a side of the cube measured in centimetres. What is the surface area when the side of the box is 5 cm?

(2) This hexagon has 9 diagonals.
Investigate the number of diagonals in different polygons.
How many diagonals are there in a polygon with n sides?

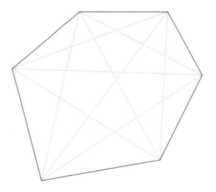

Measures and mensuration

TASK 1: Converting between units

Points to remember

⊙ Converting between metric units

  Mass   1 tonne = 1000 kg

  Area   1 hectare (ha) = 10 000 m^2

⊙ Converting between metric and imperial measurements

	Imperial to metric	**Metric to imperial**
Length	1 mile ≈ 1.6 km	1 km ≈ 0.6 miles
Mass	1 pound (lb) ≈ 0.45 kg	1 kg ≈ 2.2 pounds
Volume	1 pint ≈ 0.6 litre 1 gallon ≈ 8 pints ≈ 4.5 litres	1 litre ≈ 1.8 pints

≈ means 'is approximately equal to'.

1.   Change these measurements into the units given.

   a   90 km into m   b   4.6 m into mm

   c   35 g into kg   d   0.7 litres into ml

   e   0.56 kg into g   f   9 000 000 cm into km

2.   A rectangular football pitch has an area of 4500 m^2.
   How many hectares is this?

3.   A sports car weighs 1.622 tonnes.
   How many kilograms is this?

4.   A van can carry 4500 kg and weighs 3.5 tonnes.
   What is the weight of a full van?

5.   Josh enters a 10 km run. How many miles is this?

6 A milk tanker holds 20 500 litres of milk.
How many pints of milk could you get from the tanker?

7 A recipe for a cake needs half a pound of flour.
Roughly how many grams of flour is this?

8 The Niagara Falls has approximately 36 000 000 gallons of water falling over the edge every minute.

How many litres is that a minute?

TASK 2: Perimeter and area of triangles

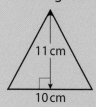
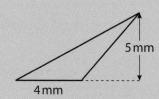
1 Calculate the area of each of these triangles.

a
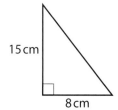

b
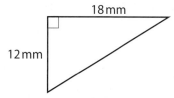

c
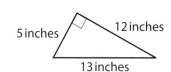

d
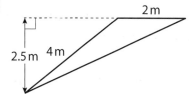

2 Find the height y of the triangle so that it has the same area as the rectangle.

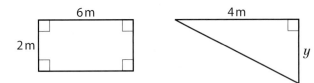

3 The area of a triangle is $19\frac{1}{2}$ square inches.
The perpendicular height is $6\frac{1}{2}$ inches.
What is the length of the base?

4   **a** Find the perimeter of this triangle.

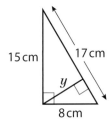

     b Find the length of the perpendicular height y in this triangle.
       Write your answer to one decimal place.

TASK 3: Perimeter and area of quadrilaterals

⊙ Points to remember

⊙ Area of a parallelogram = base × perpendicular height

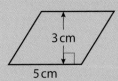

Area = 5 × 3 = 15 cm²

⊙ Area of a trapezium
$= \frac{1}{2} \times$ sum of parallel sides × perpendicular height

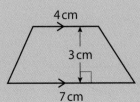

Area $= \frac{1}{2} \times (4 + 7) \times 3$
$= \frac{1}{2} \times 11 \times 3$
$= 16.5$ cm²

① Work out the area of each of these parallelograms.

a
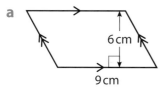
6 cm
9 cm

b
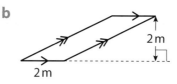
2 m
2 m

② Calculate the area of each trapezium.

a
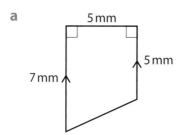
5 mm
5 mm
7 mm

b
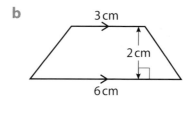
3 cm
2 cm
6 cm

c
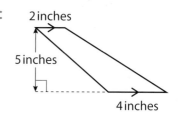
2 inches
5 inches
4 inches

③ Work out the total area of this plane shape.

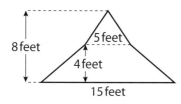
8 feet
5 feet
4 feet
15 feet

④ A trapezium has an area of 16.5 cm² and a perpendicular height of 3 cm.
One of the parallel sides is 3 cm long.
How long is the other parallel side?

TASK 4: Volume of cuboids

 Points to remember

⊙ The volume of a cuboid is length × width × height, or
area of base × height.

⊙ Volume is measured in cubic units, such as cubic millimetres (mm³),
cubic centimetres (cm³) or cubic metres (m³).

⊙ When you find the volume of a cuboid, the edges must all be in the
same units.

⊙ To find the volume of a shape made from cuboids, divide the shape up
into cuboids and add the volumes together.

1. How many single cubes make up each of these cuboids?

 single cube

a 　b 　c 　d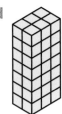

2. How many single cubes make up each of these shapes?

 single cube

a 　b 　c 　d

3. Calculate the volume of each of these cuboids.

a
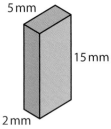
5 mm
15 mm
2 mm

b
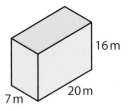
16 m
20 m
7 m

4. In the diagram the cuboid has a volume of 96 cm³.
The shaded cross-sectional area is 24 cm².
How long is the edge marked f?

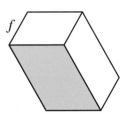

5. Calculate the volume of this shape.

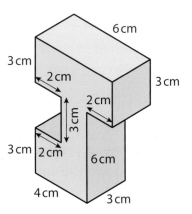

6 cm
3 cm
2 cm
3 cm
2 cm
3 cm
3 cm 2 cm
6 cm
4 cm
3 cm

TASK 5: Surface area of cuboids

Points to remember

⊙ To find the surface area of a solid, find the sum of the areas of each face.

⊙ The surface area S of a cuboid with edges of length a, b and c is given by the formula:

$$S = 2ab + 2ac + 2bc$$

⊙ Surface area is measured in square units, such as square millimetres (mm^2), square centimetres (cm^2) or square metres (m^2).

Area

m² ←÷10000 / ×10000→ cm² ←÷100 / ×100→ mm²

Volume

m³ ←÷1000000 / ×1000000→ cm³ ←÷1000 / ×1000→ mm³

---

1 Change these measurements into the units given.

a 2.5 m² to cm²

b 12 cm² to mm²

c 700 000 cm³ to m³

d 175 000 mm³ to cm³

2 Work out the surface area of each of these cuboids.

a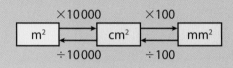
5 cm
2 cm
7 cm

b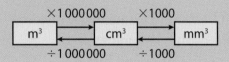
3.5 m   2.9 m
4.1 m

3 a Work out the dimensions of this cuboid.

b Work out the volume of the cuboid.

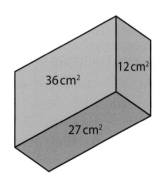
12 cm²
36 cm²
27 cm²

4 The total surface area of a cuboid is 0.94 m².
Its length is 70 cm and its width is 50 cm. Find the height of the cuboid.

TASK 1: Ordering fractions

 Points to remember

There are two ways to compare the size of two fractions, or to put several fractions in order.

1 Convert each fraction to a decimal by dividing the numerator by the denominator.
   You can use a calculator to do this.
   Then compare the decimals.

2 Change all the fractions to a common denominator.

1 Write these decimals as fractions in their simplest form.

   a 0.65   b 2.8   c 0.125   d 0.16

2 Write a fraction that is greater than 0.7 and less than 0.8.

3 Write a decimal that is greater than $\frac{4}{7}$ and less than $\frac{5}{7}$.

4 Find a fraction that is greater than $\frac{1}{4}$ and less than $\frac{3}{10}$.

5 Copy and complete these.

   a $\frac{1}{4} < \frac{\square}{24} < \frac{1}{3}$ b $\frac{7}{17} < \frac{\square}{12} < \frac{13}{31}$

6 Write these fractions as recurring decimals.

   a $\frac{5}{27}$ b $\frac{6}{11}$ c $\frac{7}{3}$ d $\frac{11}{18}$

TASK 2: Calculating with fractions

Points to remember

⊙ Multiply fractions like this:

$$\frac{21}{40} \times \frac{15}{28} = \frac{\overset{3}{\cancel{21}}}{\cancel{40}} \times \frac{\overset{3}{\cancel{15}}}{\cancel{28}_4}$$ Cancel the 21 and 28 by 7, and the 15 and 40 by 5.

$$= \frac{3 \times 3}{8 \times 4}$$ Multiply the numerators and multiply the denominators.

$$= \frac{9}{32}$$

Solve these problems **without using a calculator**. Show your working.

1 a Multiply seven eighths by three.

   b Divide sixteen twenty-fifths by four.

   c What is four fifths of seven tenths?

   d Multiply three quarters by eight ninths.

2 A rectangle measures $\frac{4}{5}$ m by $\frac{5}{8}$ m.
   What is its area in square metres?

3 Seven eighths of a pizza is cut into five equal pieces.
   What fraction of the whole pizza is each piece?

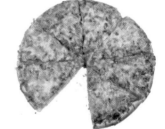

4 At a party there are several pizzas, all the same size.
   Nine boys each eat three quarters of a pizza.
   Altogether, how many pizzas do the boys eat?

5 Four sevenths of a class of pupils are girls.
   One third of the girls wear glasses.
   What fraction of the class are girls who wear glasses?

6 James poured out two fifths of a litre of orange juice into each of seven glasses.
   What is the total amount of orange juice that James poured out?

7 In Class 8, four fifths of the pupils like crisps.
   Three quarters of the pupils who like crisps also like chocolate.
   In Class 8, what fraction of the pupils like both crisps and chocolate?

8 Two thirds of a bag of sweets is shared equally among six children.
What fraction of the whole bag of sweets does each child get?

9 Three fifths of the fish in a tank are female.
Five ninths of the females are goldfish.
What fraction of the fish in the tank are female goldfish?

TASK 3: Multiplying and dividing decimals 1

 Points to remember

⊙ Multiply and divide simple decimals by using equivalent calculations.

Example 1

0.7 × 0.04

This is equivalent to $\frac{7}{10} \times \frac{4}{100} = \frac{28}{1000}$, or 0.028.

You can also think of it as 7 × 4 ÷ 10 ÷ 100 = 0.028.

There are the same number of decimal places in the answer as in the product.

Example 2

$5.6 \div 0.8 = \frac{5.6}{0.8} = \frac{5.6 \times 10}{0.8 \times 10} = \frac{56}{8} = 7$

Each number in this multiplication grid is the product of the two numbers at the top of the column and the left of the row.

×	0.3	0.4
0.5	0.15	0.2
0.9	0.27	0.36

Copy and complete these multiplication grids.

1

×	0.5	0.8
0.6		
0.2		

2

×	0.06	0.2
0.05		
0.9		

3

×		
0.4	0.012	0.28
	0.024	

TASK 4: Multiplying and dividing decimals 2

 Points to remember

When you solve word problems involving decimal measurements:

⊙ make sure that all quantities are in the same unit;

⊙ check that the answer makes sense in the context of the problem;

⊙ if appropriate, round answers to a suitable number of decimal places.

Solve these problems **without using a calculator**. Show your working.

1 **a** The diameter of a 5p coin is 1.8 centimetres.

diameter

I put six 5p coins in a row. What is the length of the row?

?

b The diameter of a 10p coin is 2.45 centimetres.
I put four 10p coins in a row. What is the length of the row?

c The length of a row of five 2p coins is 12.95 centimetres.
What is the diameter of a 2p coin?

d I make a row of alternate 2p and 5p coins. I use six coins altogether.
What is the length of the row of six coins?

2 **a** The thickness of a 10p coin is 1.85 millimetres.
I stack nine 10p coins on a table, one on top of the other.
What is the height of the stack in centimetres?

b The height of a stack of seven 5p coins is 1.19 centimetres.
What is the thickness of a 5p coin in millimetres?

c The height of a stack of nine 1p coins is 1.485 centimetres.
What is the thickness of a 1p coin in millimetres?

d A £2 coin is 2.5 mm thick. A £1 coin is 3.15 mm thick.
What is the height of a stack of three £2 coins and three £1 coins?

3 **a** A 10p coin weighs 6.5 g.
What is the total mass of eight 10p coins?

b A 2p coin weighs 7.13 g. A 1p coin weighs 3.56 g.
Eight 2p coins and eight 1p coins are placed on some scales.
What is the total mass of the coins on the scales?

TASK 5: Calculating percentages

⦿ Points to remember

⊙ Percentage means 'per hundred', or 'in every hundred'.

⊙ 47% is equivalent to $\frac{47}{100}$ or 0.47.

⊙ A quick way to find 20% of a quantity is to find 10% by
dividing by 10, then multiply the result by 2 to find 20%.
You can find 30%, 40%, 50%, … similarly.

⊙ If there is no quick method for finding a percentage of a quantity, first
find 1%, then multiply by the percentage.

⊙ Always include any units in your answer.

1 David counted 48 cars in the
school car park.
15 of them were silver.

What percentage of the cars
were silver?

2 38 of the 95 children in a primary school have at least one dental filling.
What percentage of the children don't have any fillings?

3 There are 25 pupils in a class. 64% of them are girls.

   a What fraction of the class are girls?

   b How many of the class are girls?

4 35% of the 1100 pupils in a secondary school walk to school.

   a What fraction of the pupils walk to school?

   b How many pupils do not walk to school?

5 Calculate these, giving your answer to one decimal place where appropriate.

   a 28% of 72 litres   **b** 123% of 135 km

   c 17.5% of £64   **d** 2% of 5 kg

6 Robert is taking part in a game show.
   He has been shown three amounts of money.

   £450   £500   £550

   For his prize, he must choose 75% of one amount, 70% of another amount, and 65% of the remaining amount.

   What is the maximum amount of money that Robert can win as a prize?
   What is the minimum amount?

TASK 6: Percentage increases and decreases

 Points to remember

- There are two ways of finding a new price after a percentage increase or decrease:
  - calculate the amount of increase or decrease, then add or subtract it to or from the old price;
  - add or subtract the percentage increase or decrease to or from 100%, then calculate this percentage of the original price.

- To find a percentage change given the old and new amounts, work out the amount of change as a percentage of the old amount.

You want a new tennis racket. Three shops are offering a discount on the same tennis racket.

Shop A: original cost £140, discount 35%
Shop B: original cost £110, discount 17%
Shop C: original cost £124, discount 27%

Which shop has the cheapest tennis racket?

2 Three electronics stores have announced price increases. The stores will increase their prices at the end of this month.

The current cost of the same video phone in each store, and the price increase, is shown below.

Store A: £350, increase 9%
Store B: £315, increase 21%
Store C: £365, increase 5%

Which store will sell the cheapest video phone after the end of the month?

3 Calculate the percentage change when:

a some trainers are reduced in price from £56 to £35

b a piece of elastic is stretched from 60 cm to 63 cm in length

c 350 ml of lemonade is poured out of a jug holding 900 ml of lemonade

d the charge for water for a small business increases from £940 to £987 per year

e the mass of potatoes in a sack decreases from 120 kg to 111 kg

Enquiry 1

TASK 1: Specifying the problem and planning

 Points to remember

- A **bar chart** is usually drawn on squared or graph paper. It should have:
  - a title;
  - labels for the axes;
  - evenly spaced scales starting from zero.

- If possible, the bars should be in a sensible order.
  There should be a gap between each bar.

Example

The table shows the average rainfall in London for each month of the year.

Month	Jan	Feb	Mar	Apr	May	Jun	Jul	Aug	Sep	Oct	Nov	Dec
Rainfall (mm)	49	39	39	41	47	48	59	60	52	65	60	51

Draw a bar chart to show the rainfall.

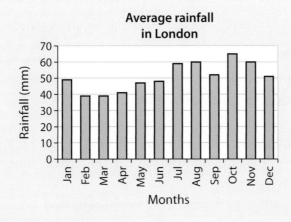

① Draw bar charts for these tables.

a Average rainfall in Paris

Month	Jan	Feb	Mar	Apr	May	Jun	Jul	Aug	Sep	Oct	Nov	Dec
Rainfall (mm)	53	54	38	34	42	67	50	62	57	55	50	49

b Average temperature in Paris

Month	Jan	Feb	Mar	Apr	May	Jun	Jul	Aug	Sep	Oct	Nov	Dec
Temperature (°C)	3	4	8	10	15	17	19	18	16	11	7	5

c Average rainfall in Bangkok

Month	Jan	Feb	Mar	Apr	May	Jun	Jul	Aug	Sep	Oct	Nov	Dec
Rainfall (mm)	11	28	30	72	189	151	158	187	320	231	57	9

d Average temperature in Bangkok

Month	Jan	Feb	Mar	Apr	May	Jun	Jul	Aug	Sep	Oct	Nov	Dec
Temperature (°C)	26	27	29	30	30	29	29	28	28	28	27	26

② Write a sentence comparing the rainfall in the two cities.

③ Write a sentence comparing the temperature in the two cities.

④ Using this information say which of the two cities you would prefer to live in.

TASK 2: Processing data

⦿ Points to remember

- The mode, median and mean are different ways of finding the average of a set of numbers. The range shows how much the numbers are spread out.
- The **mode** is the number that occurs most often in the set.
- The **mean** is found by adding up all the numbers in the set and dividing by the number of numbers in the set.
- The **median** is the middle number, or the mean of the middle two numbers, when all the numbers in the set are arranged in order.
- The **range** is the highest number in the set minus the lowest number.

Example

Ten pupils took a spelling test and got these scores:

3, 8, 5, 9, 10, 4, 7, 8, 4, 8.

The mean is:

(3 + 8 + 5 + 9 + 10 + 4 + 7 + 8 + 4 + 8) ÷ 10 = 66 ÷ 10 = 6.6.

The scores in order are: 3, 4, 4, 5, 7, 8, 8, 8, 9, 10.
The middle pair are 7 and 8 so the median is 7.5.

The mode is 8.

The range is 10 − 3 = 7.

The data in this task is from www.studentsoftheworld.info.

(1) The table shows the mean monthly temperature in °C in three countries.

Country	Jan	Feb	Mar	Apr	May	Jun	Jul	Aug	Sep	Oct	Nov	Dec
Indonesia	25	25	26	26	26	26	26	25	26	26	26	25
United Kingdom	5	6	7	10	13	16	18	18	16	13	9	6
Venezuela	15	21	21	23	23	22	22	22	22	22	21	20

a Work out the mean temperature over the year for each country.

b Work out the modal temperature in each country.

c Work out the range of the temperature in each country.

d In which country is the mode a very good description of the average temperature? Why?

e Write a sentence explaining what the range tells you about the temperature in the three countries.

Autumn in the UK.

(2) The table shows the mean monthly rainfall in mm in three countries.

Country	Jan	Feb	Mar	Apr	May	Jun	Jul	Aug	Sep	Oct	Nov	Dec
Indonesia	326	235	198	133	112	90	57	50	77	89	149	180
United Kingdom	42	31	38	40	46	48	42	52	53	43	54	48
Venezuela	23	28	10	44	89	111	108	107	107	130	69	48

a   Work out the mean rainfall over the year for each country.

b   Why is the mode not a very useful average to use with rainfall data?

c   Work out the median for each country.

d   Which country has a median that is not very useful? Why?

TASK 3: Representing data

● Points to remember

⊙ A **two-way table** can be read both across the page and down.
It allows two types of information to be presented and compared in the same form.

⊙ A table showing the distances between places is a particular kind of two-way table.

Example

The table shows the distances in miles between some places in south-west England.

To find the distance between two places, find the places in the list.
Read one across and the other down the page.
The distance between the two is where the row and column meet.

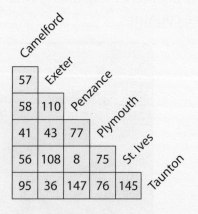

The distance between Penzance and Plymouth is 77 miles.

Exeter and St. Ives are 108 miles apart.

The town that is furthest from Camelford is Taunton.

1 The table shows the distances
in miles between some capital
cities in Europe.

	Oslo	Brussels	Dublin	Rome	Athens	Kiev
Brussels	675					
Dublin	783	484				
Rome	1252	735	1182			
Athens	1619	1298	1777	646		
Kiev	1012	1141	1563	1039	923	
Warsaw	646	727	1135	839	1013	429

a How far apart are Oslo and Kiev?

b How far apart are Brussels and Athens?

c Which two cities are furthest apart?

d Which two cities are nearest?

e Which two pairs of cities are the same distance apart?

f A driving tour takes the route:
   Rome – Athens – Warsaw – Kiev – Brussels – Rome.
   How many miles is the driving tour in total?

2 The two-way table shows the test results for three Year 8 classes.

Class	Grade					Totals
	A	B	C	D	E	
8A	4	2	6	8	3	23
8B	7	8	12	2	0	29
8C	0	9	10	8	0	27
Totals	11	19	28	18	3	

a How many pupils are there in the three classes in total?

b Which class got the most grade As?

c The pass grades are A, B and C.
   Which class had the most pass grades?

TASK 4: Interpreting data

 Points to remember

A **scatter graph** is used to look for connections between two quantities. One quantity is put on the horizontal axis and the other on the vertical axis. Each point on the scatter graph represents a pair of values.

- ⊙ The scatter graph needs a title.
- ⊙ Use a ruler and pencil.
- ⊙ Label the lines on the axes evenly and write what the quantity is next to the axis.

Example

The table shows the wind speed and temperature for some places in Scotland in April.

Temperature (°C)	10	9	10	7	9	12	9	7	10	9	11	9	9	8	9	8	9
Wind speed (knots)	20	10	13	17	11	17	19	27	7	6	14	15	14	16	22	13	15

The scatter graph shows the wind speed plotted against the temperature.

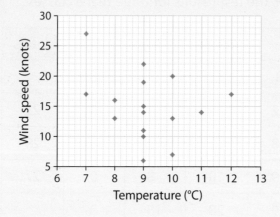

You will need graph paper, a pencil and a ruler.

1 The table shows the temperature and wind speed for some places in England.

Temperature (°C)	12	8	10	10	11	10	10	11	7	8	9	11	10	8	8	5	10
Wind speed (knots)	18	19	17	12	12	19	5	9	5	9	9	8	8	6	1	4	1

Draw a scatter graph to look for a connection between temperature and wind speed.
Put temperature on the horizontal axis with a scale of 2 cm to 1°C from 4 to 13°C.
Put wind speed on the vertical axis with a scale of 1 cm to 1 knot from 0 to 20 knots.

2 The table shows the temperature and wind speed for places across the world.

Temperature (°C)	21	12	9	13	28	8	6	26	26	22	29	17	23	31	6	31	20
Wind speed (knots)	13	10	8	15	10	8	5	4	8	9	14	5	7	10	4	9	10

Draw a scatter graph to look for a connection between the temperature and
wind speed.
Put temperature on the horizontal axis with a scale of 2 cm to 5°C from 5 to 35°C.
Put wind speed on the vertical axis with a scale of 2 cm to 1 knot from 4 to 16 knots.

3 What could you use these graphs to find out about?

TASK 5: Comparing groups

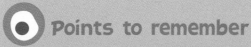

Points to remember

⊙ Simple statistics and a range of charts, graphs and tables are useful for making comparisons between sets of data.

Collect some data ready to discuss in school.

Ask the following questions to five people, some adults and some children, that you know outside of school. Keep the answers for each person separate.

① How many books have you read in the last month?

② How much do you like reading: very much, quite a lot, a bit, or not at all?

③ How often do you read for pleasure: every day or almost every day, once or twice a week, once or twice a month, never or almost never?

④ What types of books do you like?

⑤ What other sources of reading material do you read?
For example, magazines, newspapers, catalogues, email, texts, etc.

Write down whether each person you ask is male or female and their age.

TASK 6: Presenting results

Points to remember

⊙ Choose an appropriate graph or chart for the data you are representing.

⊙ Different types of graph are useful for different purposes because they show the data in different ways.

The table shows some information about a holiday resort in the south-west of England.

	Jan	Feb	Mar	Apr	May	Jun	Jul	Aug	Sep	Oct	Nov	Dec
Average temperature (°C)	6	6	6.9	9.1	11.8	14.6	16.2	16.2	14.5	11.5	8.4	6.8
Total rainfall (mm)	106.7	82.9	78	55.5	62.3	55.4	62.4	73.2	77.2	92.7	107.4	113.3
Number of visitors	300	400	900	3800	2700	4100	5100	5200	3600	2100	300	1400

1 Draw some graphs to illustrate the data.

2 Write a sentence about each of the temperature, rainfall and number of visitors to describe how they change over the course of a year.

3 Decide which month would be most suitable for a holiday for each of the following and explain your answer.

   a A young family who like the sunshine but don't have to go in the school holidays

   b Someone who doesn't mind the weather but wants some peace and quiet

   c Someone going on a walking holiday who would like as little rain as possible

4 When would you visit the holiday resort? Why?

Functions and graphs

TASK 1: Plotting points

> **⊙ Points to remember**
>
> A **coordinate pair** is an ordered pair of numbers (x, y).
> - ⊙ The **x-coordinate** is along the horizontal x-axis.
> - ⊙ The **y-coordinate** is up the vertical y-axis.

You will need squared paper, pencil and ruler.

1 Write down the coordinates of the points marked on the grid below.

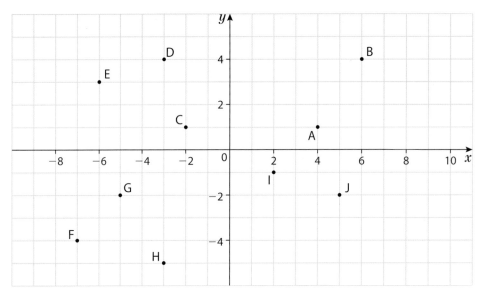

2 Before you start each of these, think about what values of x and y you need and draw a grid.

   a Points P (2, 1) and Q (−3, 6) are two opposite vertices of a square.
   What are the coordinates of the other two vertices?
   (There is one solution.)

   b The same points P (2, 1) and Q (−3, 6) are adjacent vertices of a square.
   What are the coordinates of the other two vertices?
   (There are two solutions. Find both of them.)

TASK 2: Functions and inverse functions

 Points to remember

⊙ You can show a relationship between two variables x and y in a
mapping diagram like this:

$x \rightarrow y$
$1 \rightarrow 6$
$2 \rightarrow 10$
$3 \rightarrow 14$
$4 \rightarrow 18$
$x \rightarrow 4x + 2$

⊙ You can also write it as a **function** like this:

$x \rightarrow$ | multiply by 4 | $\rightarrow$ | add 2 | $\rightarrow y$

⊙ The **inverse function** is:

$x \leftarrow$ | divide by 4 | $\leftarrow$ | subtract 2 | $\leftarrow y$

---

1 Find the outputs y for the given inputs x for this function:

$x \rightarrow$ | multiply by 8 | $\rightarrow$ | add 3 | $\rightarrow y$

a $x = 2$ b $x = 5$ c $x = 7$ d $x = 10$

e $x = 9$ f $x = 8$ g $x = 0.5$ h $x = 0.2$

2 Work out the functions and find the missing numbers in these mappings.

a $x \rightarrow y$ b $x \rightarrow y$
  $1 \rightarrow 6$ $1 \rightarrow 5$
  $2 \rightarrow 11$ $2 \rightarrow 12$
  $3 \rightarrow 16$ $3 \rightarrow 19$
  $4 \rightarrow$ $4 \rightarrow$
  $5 \rightarrow$ $5 \rightarrow$
  $6 \rightarrow$ $6 \rightarrow$
  $x \rightarrow$ $x \rightarrow$

3 Write the inverse functions of these.

a $x \rightarrow$ | multiply by 15 | $\rightarrow$ | subtract 9 | $\rightarrow y$

b $x \rightarrow$ | divide by 4 | $\rightarrow$ | add 8 | $\rightarrow y$

c $x \rightarrow$ | subtract 6 | $\rightarrow$ | multiply by 17 | $\rightarrow y$

TASK 3: Functions, equations and graphs

 Points to remember

- You can show a relationship between two variables x and y in a mapping diagram, as a function, as an equation or as a graph.

- A **linear equation** has terms in x but not x^2 or any higher power.

- You can draw an accurate graph to represent a linear equation by finding three pairs of values (x, y) and plotting them on rectangular axes.

- A **linear graph** is always a straight-line graph.

- Inspect relationships carefully to see whether they are linear or more complex functions.

Example

x	0	1	2
$y = 3x + 1$	-1	2	5

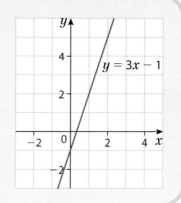

You will need squared paper, ruler and pencil.

1. Copy and complete these tables.

x	-3	-2	-1	0	1	2	3	4
$y = 2x + 1$								

x	-1.5	-1	-0.5	0	0.5	1	1.5	2
$y = 8x - 3$								

x	0.1	0.2	0.3	0.4	0.5	0.6	0.7	0.8
$y = 6x + 1$								

2 On squared paper, draw accurate graphs of these linear equations.

    a $y = 2x$ **b** $y = 3x - 1$ **c** $y = x + 4$ **d** $y = 5x - 2$

TASK 4: Sketching graphs

Points to remember

- Graphs of the form $y = ax$, where a is a constant, are straight-line graphs that pass through the origin.
  - The steepness of the line is called its **gradient**.
  - The number in front of x is called the **coefficient** of x. The larger the coefficient of x, the greater the gradient.

- A **sketch** of a graph is a neat drawing that gives an indication of some of its features.

You will need squared paper, pencil and ruler.

1 On squared paper, **sketch** the graphs of these equations on separate sets of axes.

    a $y = x$ **b** $y = x - 3$ **c** $y = x + 7$ **d** $y = 3x - 2$

    e $y = 5x + 4$ **f** $y = 0.5x + 1$ **g** $y = -x$ **h** $y = -2x + 3$

2 Explain how you know how to sketch the graph of $y = -4x - 5$.

3 Explain what is meant by a *linear graph*.

TASK 5: Interpreting equations of graphs

Points to remember

- Every linear function can be represented as a straight-line graph with an equation of the form $y = ax + b$.

- The **gradient** of the graph is a and the **intercept** on the y-axis is $(0, b)$.

Example

Look at this linear equation: $y = 3x + 4$.

The equation is in the form $y = ax + b$.

The coefficient of x is 3.
The gradient of the graph of this equation is 3.

The intercept of the graph with the y-axis is $(0, 4)$.

1. Write down the gradient and intercept with the y-axis of the graph of each of these linear equations.

   a $y = x$

   c $y = 3x + 13$

   e $y = -x + 3$

   g $y = -x - 9$

   b $y = 7x + 5$

   d $y = 8x - 7$

   f $y = 0.5x + 6$

   h $y = \frac{1}{2}x - \frac{1}{6}$

2. Write down the equations of these linear graphs.

   a Gradient 2, intercept $(0, 5)$

   c Gradient 9, intercept $(0, -8)$

   e Gradient -4, intercept $(0, 3)$

   b Gradient 0, intercept $(0, 14)$

   d Gradient 0.5, intercept $(0, -0.5)$

   f Gradient -1, intercept $(0, -5)$

TASK 6: Interpreting real-life graphs 1

 Points to remember

- A **distance-time graph** or **travel graph** describes stages in a journey.

- A **conversion graph** shows how to change one unit to another.

- When you draw or interpret graphs of real situations, take care with the scales on the axes.

① This graph represents a walk that Lauren did with her friends.

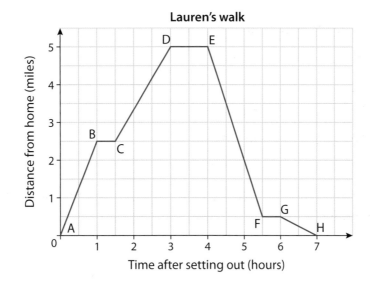

Lauren's walk

a Lauren set out with her friends from her home (A) at 10:30 am.
At what time did they make their first stop at B?

b How far had they walked from A to B?

c For how long did they stop?

d At what time did they arrive at their second stop (D)?

e Lauren and her friends had lunch and after an hour they set off for home.
They walked to Lauren's friend's house (F).
How far was it to her friend's house?

f At what time did Lauren arrive home?

g On which section of the walk did they walk fastest?

h What was the average speed (in miles per hour) on the fastest section?

Proportional reasoning

TASK 1: Dividing a quantity in a given ratio

● Points to remember

⊙ A **proportion** is a fraction or percentage. If 1 in every 4 beads is red, the proportion of red beads is $\frac{1}{4}$ or 25%.

⊙ A **ratio** is a way of comparing quantities.
We usually use whole numbers in a ratio and write them without units.

⊙ Ratios are simplified like fractions.

⊙ To divide a quantity into two parts in the ratio $a : b$, begin by dividing the quantity into $a + b$ equal shares.
Put a shares in one part, and b shares in the other part.
This is the same as finding the fractions $\dfrac{a}{a + b}$ and $\dfrac{b}{a + b}$ of the quantity.

1. Copy and complete this diagram.
   Write ratios equivalent to the one in the centre in the empty boxes.

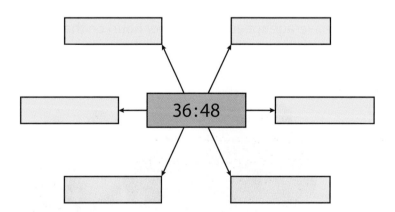

(2) Divide £120 in each of these ratios.

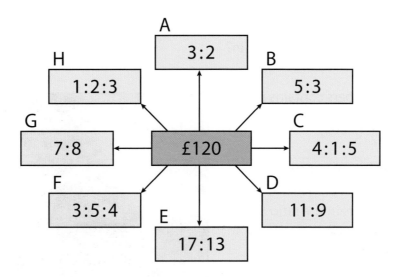

TASK 2: Solving ratio problems

> **⦿ Points to remember**
>
> ⦿ A **unitary ratio** is written in the form $1 : m$.
> To convert a ratio of $2 : 15$ to a unitary ratio, divide by 2 to get $1 : 7.5$.
>
> ⦿ Unitary ratios are useful for comparing ratios.
>
> ⦿ A **scale factor** tells you how many times bigger one number is than another.

Example

An orange weighs 200 g and a banana weighs 400 g.

The ratio of the mass of the orange to the mass of the banana is $1 : 2$.
The mass of the banana is twice that of the orange.
The mass of the orange is half of the mass of the apple.

(1) Gopal and Jyoti have 140 paperbacks altogether.
Jyoti has three times as many as Gopal.
How many paperbacks do each of them have?

2　Harry and Sophie are both goalkeepers.
Last season, Harry let in twice as many goals as Sophie.
Altogether, they let in 36 goals.
How many goals did Harry let in?

3　A box of peppers contains red peppers and green peppers in the ratio 2 : 5.

A second box of peppers contains red peppers and green peppers in the ratio 5 : 9.

Which box has the greater proportion of green peppers?

4　The ratio of goals for to goals against for two football teams is:

　　City　　7 : 2
　Rovers　18 : 5

Which team is more successful? Explain your answer.

5　The ratio of brown to white loaves sold by a bakery one day last week was 5 : 4.
The bakery sold 65 brown loaves.
How many white loaves did the bakery sell?

6　The ratio of adults to children watching a film in a cinema is 7 : 3.
There are 135 children watching the film.
How many adults are watching it?

7　Amy, Ben and Rachel share some money in ratio of 2 : 5 : 6.
Ben's share is £40.

a　How much money is Amy's share?

b　How much money is Rachel's share?

8　A patch of grass has daisies, buttercups and dandelions in the ratio 8 : 4 : 1.
There are 24 buttercups.
How many daisies, buttercups and dandelions are there altogether in the patch of grass?

TASK 3: Scale drawings

> ### ⦿ Points to remember
>
> ⦿ A map ratio is the ratio of the distance on the map to the actual distance on the ground.
>
> ⦿ Map ratios are always given in the form $1 : n$ and have no units. For example, a scale of 1 cm to 50 m is a map ratio of 1 : 5000, since 50 m is 5000 cm.
>
> ⦿ A distance 'as the crow flies' is the shortest distance between two points, measured as a straight line.

1   This is a map of the area around Whitby. The map scale is 1 : 100 000.

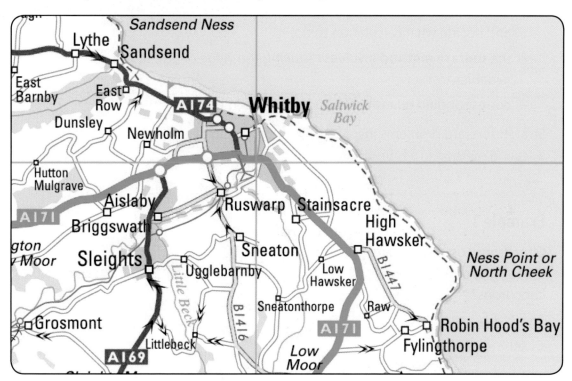

a   What distance does 1 cm on the map represent?

b   The red dashed line represents a footpath. Estimate the actual distance along the footpath from Whitby to Robin Hood's Bay. Use a piece of string.

c   What is the actual direct distance 'as the crow flies':
from Whitby to Sleights?
from Lythe to Robin Hood's Bay?

d   The A171 road is marked in green on the map. Use your string to estimate how far it is to drive along the A171 from High Hawsker to Aislaby.

2 Write each of these scales as a map ratio.

 a 2 cm to 1 km   b 1 cm to 200 km   c 1 cm to 5 km   d 2 cm to 25 m

3 The ratio of a map is 1 : 150 000.
The distance between two cities on the map is 9 cm.
What is the actual distance between the two cities?

TASK 4: The unitary method

> **◉ Points to remember**
>
> ◉ When you solve direct proportion problems:
> - a four-cell diagram helps you to see relationships between numbers and decide what calculation to do;
> - the **unitary method** involves reducing the value of one of the variables to 1;
> - corresponding quantities must be in the same units.
>
> Straightforward problems involving direct proportion can be solved using a scaling method in a four-cell diagram.

Example 1

Chocdrops cost £1.60 for 75 g.
What is the cost of 300 g of chocdrops?

300 g of chocdrops cost
£1.60 × 4 = £6.40.

Cost (£)	Chocdrops (g)	
1.60	75	
?	300	× 4

Harder problems can be solved using the unitary method.

Example 2

The mass of 120 ml of olive oil is 90 g.
What is the mass of 58 ml of olive oil?

58 ml of olive oil has a mass of 43.5 g.

Oil (ml)	Mass (g)	
120	90	
1	0.75	÷ 120
58	43.5	× 58

Answer question 1 **without using a calculator**.

1. This recipe makes fish pie for 4 people.

   a Write down the ingredients to make fish pie for 10 people.

   b What is the ratio of the amounts of ingredients to make fish pie for 4 people to the amounts for 10 people?

   Lena makes fish pie using 175 g of cheese.

   c How many people will Lena's fish pie feed?

   d Write down the other ingredients for Lena's fish pie.

RECIPE FOR FISH PIE FOR 4 PEOPLE

320 g haddock
120 ml milk
1 kg potatoes
100 g cheese
1 tablespoon flour

For questions 2 and 3, you may **use a calculator**.

2. £1 is about the same as 1.9 US dollars ($).

   a How many dollars do you get for £28?

   b How many pounds do you get for $285?

3. A train is travelling at an average speed of 66 miles per hour.

   a How far has the train travelled after 4 hours?

   b How far has the train travelled after 20 minutes?

   c How long will it take the train to travel 165 miles?

TASK 5: Fraction, decimal and percentage operators

Points to remember

- An operation can be described in different ways.
  For example, for $16 \rightarrow 10$, the relationship could be described as
  $\times 5$ then $\div 8$, $\times \frac{5}{8}$, $\times 0.625$, $\times 62.5\%$, $\div 1.6$.
- When you solve problems involving fractions, decimals and percentages, decide which is the most efficient way to calculate.
- The calculation $\frac{5}{8}$ of 10 can also be described as:
  - multiply 10 by 5 then divide by 8
  - multiply 10 by 0.625
  - find 6.25% of 10
  - divide 10 by 1.6.

Example

Find 65% of £82.

You can use your calculator to calculate $\frac{65}{100}$ of £82:

⑥⑤÷①⓪⓪×⑧②=

or you can use fewer keys to calculate 0.65×82:

⓪・⑥⑤×⑧②=

1 Copy and complete this table.

Percentage	70%	30%	20%	2%	80%	45%	15%	12%
Fraction in its simplest form	$\frac{7}{10}$							
Decimal	0.7							

2 **Use your calculator** to work out answers to these calculations. Remember to include the units in your answers.

a 42% of 60 m

b 58% of £95

c 39% of 4.5 km

d 68% of £72.50

e 105% of 3.2 litres

f 226% of 84 kg

g $\frac{4}{5}$ of 8 cm

h $\frac{3}{4}$ of £9.28

i $\frac{7}{10}$ of £36.50

TASK 6: Solving problems

 Points to remember

⊙ When you solve problems involving fractions, decimals and percentages, choose a calculation method that is easy to use with the numbers in the problem.

Ram's Record Shop has a sale of CDs.

1   Ram keeps a note on how many CDs are bought each day in the sale.

	Mon	Tues	Wed	Thurs	Fri	Sat	Total
hip-hop	34	37	42	40	43	95	291
pop	35	24	20	48	24	65	216
rap	11	14	8	12	13	17	75
Total	80	75	70	100	80	177	582

a What percentage of Monday's sales were hip-hop CDs?

b What percentage of Tuesday's sales were pop CDs?

c What percentage of the total sales for rap did Ram sell on Thursday?

d What percentage of the week's sales were hip-hop?

2   Find the sale price of each of these CDs.

a Classical: usual price £15.00

b Pop: usual price £11.80

c Rock: usual price £12.80

d Spiritual and gospel: usual price £11.50

e Hip-hop: usual price £10.60

f World music: usual price £14.75

g Rap: usual price £8.20

h Jazz: usual price £13.20

i Country and western: usual price £12.00

j Blues: usual price £9.50

Ram's Records
CD SALE
Massive Discounts!

15% off
pop, rap, hip-hop

12% off
classical, spiritual & gospel

16% off
blues, country & western

5% off
jazz, rock

28% off
world music

Transformations

G 4.3

TASK 1: Repeated transformations

Points to remember

- After reflection, rotation or translation, the object and image are congruent.

Translation

- All points of the object move the same distance in the same direction.

- Repeated translations can be replaced by a single translation.

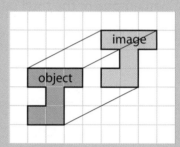

Reflection

- Corresponding points of the object and image are the same perpendicular distance from the line of reflection but on opposite sides of it.

- Together, the object and image form a symmetrical pattern about the line of reflection.

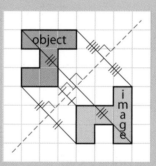

Rotation

- To describe a rotation you must give an angle and a direction (clockwise or anticlockwise), and a centre of rotation.

- All points of the object move through the same angle.

- Repeated rotations about the same centre of rotation can be replaced by a single rotation.

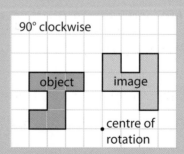

Wallpaper patterns are often based on:

reflections,   rotations,   or translations.

   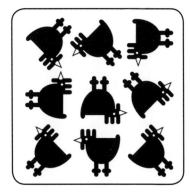   

The pattern below was created by repeatedly reflecting this tile.

① Create your own wallpaper pattern.
Copy this grid on squared paper.

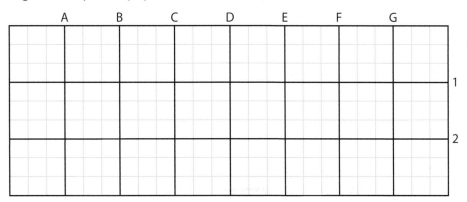

In the top left 3 by 3 square, colour 5 of the 9 squares to create a pattern.
Reflect this pattern in **line A**.
Now reflect this image in **line B** and repeat this until the top row is complete.

Now reflect the top row in **line 1** and then reflect this second row in **line 2**.

Describe the single transformation to move the pattern in the top left corner to:

a   the first 3 by 3 square in the bottom row;

b   the second 3 by 3 square in the second row;

c   the fifth 3 by 3 square in the bottom row.

②   If possible, use ICT. Start by creating a pattern, either using a drawing package or by taking a photograph. Place your image in the top left-hand square and then reflect it as above.

TASK 2: Combining transformations

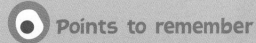

Points to remember

⊙ Reflections, rotations and translations can be combined to transform an object.

⊙ Transformations can be combined in any order.

⊙ Different combinations of transformations may have different effects.

You will need squared paper, a sharp pencil and a ruler.

①   Copy this diagram on squared paper.
Reflect the object in the x-axis
and then reflect this image in the
y-axis.
What single transformation
would create the same effect?

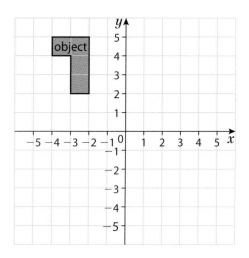

②   Copy the diagram for question 1 on another piece of squared paper.
Rotate the image through 90° clockwise about the origin.
Then reflect the image in the x-axis.

③   Write down the coordinates of the image of point A (3, 4) after a reflection in the y-axis followed by a rotation through 90° clockwise about the origin.
You may wish to draw a set of axes to help you.

TASK 3: Using ICT to explore transformations

⊙ Tessellations can be generated by using reflections, rotations or translations.

⊙ Some regular polygons will tessellate, e.g. equilateral triangles, squares, regular hexagons.

⊙ Some regular polygons will not tessellate, e.g. regular pentagons.

⊙ Some regular polygons will tessellate when combined with other regular polygons, e.g. octagons and squares.

You will need squared paper.

1   Use squared paper.

    a   Draw a diagram to show how this shape will tessellate.

       Your tessellation should have at least ten shapes.

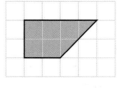

    b   Draw a diagram to show how this shape will tessellate.

       Your tessellation should have at least ten shapes.

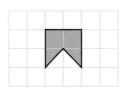

2   **a**   Draw a diagram to show how an isosceles triangle could tessellate.

    b   Explain why it is possible to create a tessellation of an isosceles triangle

3   The interior angle of a regular pentagon is 108°.
    Explain why it is not possible to create a tessellation of a regular pentagon.

4   **a**   Draw a diagram to show how to create a tessellation of a square and an equilateral triangle with sides of the same length as the sides of the square.

    b   Each angle of a square is 90° and each angle of an equilateral triangle is 60°.
       Explain why it is possible to tessellate squares and equilateral triangles without leaving any gaps.

TASK 4: Scale factor

Example

The image is an enlargement of the object.

a What is the scale factor of the enlargement?

b What are the coordinates of the centre of enlargement?

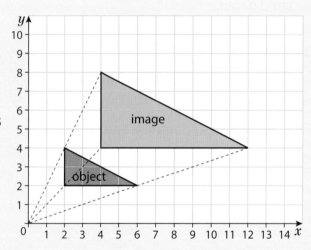

a Each side of the object triangle has doubled in length, so the scale factor is 2.

b By joining corresponding points of the object and image, and extending the lines until they meet, we see that the centre of enlargement is the point (0, 0).

You will need squared paper.

1 Write down the scale factor that links each pair of similar shapes.

a
5 cm | object
10 cm | image

b
object
13 mm
image
39 mm

c
image
24 cm
object
12 cm

d
object
radius = 4 cm
image
radius = 6 cm

2 Copy this diagram on squared paper. Enlarge the object by a scale factor of 2 so that point A is transformed to point A'.

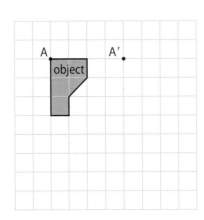

3 The image is an enlargement of the object.

a What is the scale factor of the enlargement?

b What are the coordinates of the centre of enlargement?

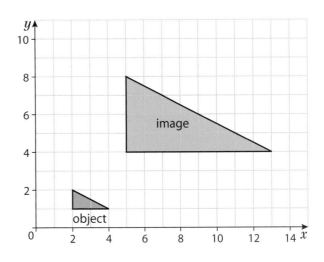

TASK 5: Centre of enlargement

Points to remember

For an enlargement of scale factor 2:

⊙ the length of each side of the object is multiplied by 2;

⊙ the distance from the centre of enlargement to each point on the object is multiplied by 2.

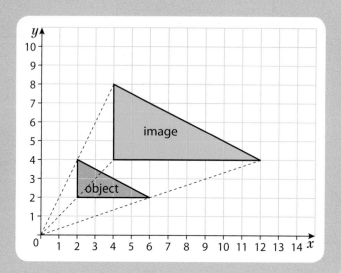

You will need squared paper.

1. Copy this diagram on squared paper.

   Enlarge the object by a scale factor of 2 from each of the centres of enlargement A and B.

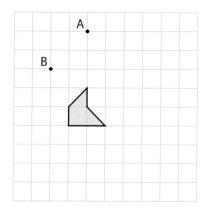

2. Look at the diagram.

   Describe fully the single transformation that transforms shape A to shape B.

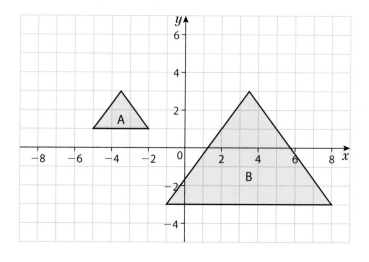

TASK 6: Enlargement, ratio and proportion

  Points to remember

- ⊙ Similar shapes are enlargements of each other.

- ⊙ All angles remain unaltered by an enlargement.

- ⊙ Lengths in the object are multiplied by the scale factor to find corresponding lengths in the image.

- ⊙ The unitary method can be used to calculate missing lengths.

1 Find the missing lengths in these pairs of similar shapes.

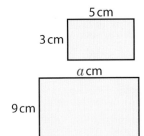

a

5 cm

3 cm

a cm

9 cm

b

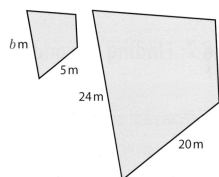

b m

5 m

24 m

20 m

c

7 cm

c cm

2 cm

16 cm

2 Look at these two rectangles.

Is the bigger rectangle an enlargement of the smaller rectangle?

Explain how you know.

10 cm

16 cm

5 cm

8 cm

③ The bigger shape is an enlargement of the smaller shape.

a What is the scale factor?

b What are the coordinates of the centre of enlargement?

c How many times bigger is the perimeter of the image than the perimeter of the object?

d How many times bigger is the area of the image than the area of the object?

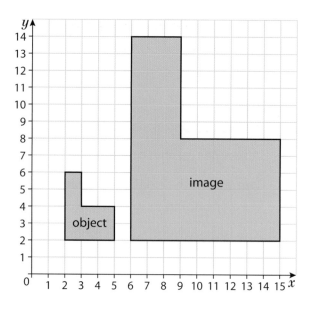

TASK 7: Finding the midpoint

 Points to remember

Given a line segment AB:

⊙ the x-coordinate of the midpoint M is the mean of the x-coordinates of A and B;
x-coordinate of M $= \left(\dfrac{1+7}{2}\right) = \dfrac{8}{2} = 4$

⊙ the y-coordinate of the midpoint M is the mean of the y-coordinates of A and B.
y-coordinate of M $= \left(\dfrac{3+5}{2}\right) = \dfrac{8}{2} = 4$

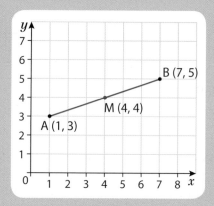

So M is the point (4, 4).

1 What are the coordinates of the midpoint of each of these line segments?

a AB

b CD

c EF

d GH

e IJ

f KL

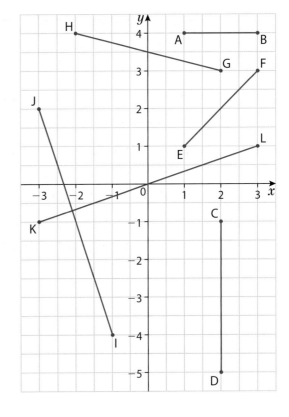

 2 Calculate the coordinates of the midpoint of the line segment joining these points:

a point C $(5, -4)$ to point D $(3, 6)$

b point X $(-5, 3)$ to point Y $(-7, -7)$

 3 The midpoint of line segment FG has coordinates $(4, 1)$.
Point F has coordinates $(7, 0)$.
What are the coordinates of point G?

 4 The midpoint M of the line segment DE has coordinates $(x, 4)$.
D has coordinates $(-1, y)$ and E has coordinates $(11, 7)$.
What are the values of x and y?

TASK 1: Functions, equations and graphs

⊙ Points to remember

⊙ A function machine applies a rule or **function** to an **input** x and gives the related **output** y.

For example, when the input $x = 4$ is put through the function $x \rightarrow$ | multiply by 6 | $\rightarrow$ | add 5 | $\rightarrow y$, the output y is 29.

⊙ This function can be written as the equation $y = 6x + 5$.

⊙ You can draw a graph of this linear equation. All the points on the graph are solutions of the equation.

① This is the graph of the equation of $y = 2x + 3$.

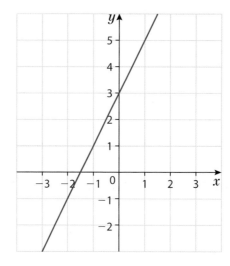

Use the graph to estimate the value of y for each of these values of x.

a $x = 0$ b $x = 1$ c $x = -1$

d $x = -2$ e $x = 0.5$ f $x = -1.5$

(2) Write these functions as equations in x and y.

a $x \rightarrow$ | add 36 | $\rightarrow y$

b $x \rightarrow$ | subtract 23 | $\rightarrow y$

c $x \rightarrow$ | multiply by 24 | $\rightarrow y$

d $x \rightarrow$ | divide by 15 | $\rightarrow y$

e $x \rightarrow$ | multiply by 7 | $\rightarrow$ | add 41 | $\rightarrow y$

f $x \rightarrow$ | multiply by 72 | $\rightarrow$ | subtract 53 | $\rightarrow y$

g $x \rightarrow$ | divide by 7 | $\rightarrow$ | add 32 | $\rightarrow y$

h $x \rightarrow$ | divide by 17.5 | $\rightarrow$ | subtract 6 | $\rightarrow y$

TASK 2: Solving linear equations

⊙ Points to remember

⊙ The equation $x + 16 = 31$ has a unique solution.

⊙ To solve the equation you can use the inverse function.

$$x + 16 = 31 \qquad\qquad x \rightarrow \boxed{+ 16} \rightarrow 31$$

subtract 16 $\qquad x = 15 \qquad\qquad 15 \leftarrow \boxed{- 16} \leftarrow 31$

⊙ What you do to one side of the equation you must do to the other to keep the equation in balance.

(1) How many solutions are there to the equation $y = 5x - 2$?

(2) How many solutions are there to the equation $5x - 2 = 18$?

(3) Find the value of x in each of these equations.

a $x + 16 = 53$ b $x - 27 = 4$

c $x + 47 = 61$ d $x + 7.5 = 8$

e $x - 4 = 4$ f $x + 18 = 16$

g $13 + x = 25$ h $13 - x = 7$

4   Find the value of x in each of these equations.

      a $16x = 48$ **b** $9x = 63$

      c $4x = 52$ **d** $12x = 132$

      e $\dfrac{x}{4} = 7$ **f** $\dfrac{x}{6} = 8$

      g $\dfrac{x}{2} = 19$ **h** $\dfrac{x}{3} = 5$

TASK 3: More linear equations

> ## ◉ Points to remember
>
> ◉ The equation $y = 3x + 5$ has an infinite number of solutions. Any point (x, y) on its graph is a solution.
>
> ◉ The equation $3x + 5 = 17$ has a unique solution.
>
> ◉ To solve the equation use the inverse function:
>
> $3x + 5 = 17$ $x \rightarrow \boxed{\times 3} \rightarrow \boxed{+ 5} \rightarrow 17$
>
> subtract 5 $3x = 17$ $4 \leftarrow \boxed{\div 3} \leftarrow \boxed{- 5} \leftarrow 17$
>
> divide by 3 $\underline{x = 4}$
>
> ◉ What you do to one side of the equation you must do to the other to keep the equation in balance.

(1)   **a** Write an equation in x.

      b Solve the equation and work out the value of each of the angles.

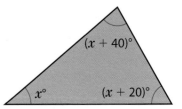

(2)   Find the value of x in each of these equations.

      a $3x + 16 = 43$ **b** $4x + 7 = 9$

      c $7x - 8 = 13$ **d** $6x - 13 = 17$

      e $8x - 17 = 39$ **f** $10x + 4 = 6$

      g $\dfrac{x}{4} + 7 = 10$ **h** $\dfrac{x}{9} - 2 = 1$

TASK 4: Forming equations and formulae

Points to remember

- You can use algebra to solve problems.
- Read through the problem carefully and write an equation.
- Solve the equation, then go back and use this to solve the problem.

1 Write equations to match these statements then solve the equations.

   a Let a number be w. Multiply it by 6, then add 31. The answer is 121.

   b Let a number be x. Divide it by 3, then add 42. The answer is 46.

   c Let a number be y. Multiply it by 14, then subtract 35. The answer is 91.

   d Let a number be z. Add 5, then multiply the result by 8. The answer is 96.

2 Sam is x years old. His sister is 17 and his granddad is 73.
If you add four times Sam's age to his sister's age, you get his granddad's age.
How old is Sam?

3 Peanuts are sold in three different packs.
In the smallest pack there are y peanuts.
There are 27 more peanuts in the
middle-size pack.
In the largest pack there are three times
as many as in the smallest pack.

There are 152 peanuts altogether in the three
packs. How many peanuts are in each pack?

4 Alice gets £x pocket money each month.
Daisy gets twice as much pocket money as Alice.
Becka gets £5 more pocket money than Daisy.
Altogether they get £95 pocket money a month.
How much does each girl get?

5 Find three consecutive numbers whose sum is 252.

Extension problem

6 Is the sum of four even numbers always divisible by 4?

TASK 5: Equations with brackets

 Points to remember

⊙ There are two ways of solving equations with single brackets (see the example below).

⊙ When you have more complex equations, multiply out any brackets and simplify the equation before you work through a solution.

Example

Solve $5(x + 4) = 55$.

Method 1: Leave the brackets in the equation.

$$5(x + 4) = 55$$

divide by 5 $\quad x + 4 = 11$

subtract 4 $\quad \underline{x = 7}$

$$x \rightarrow \boxed{+ 4} \rightarrow \boxed{\times 5} \rightarrow 55$$
$$7 \leftarrow \boxed{- 4} \leftarrow \boxed{\div 5} \leftarrow 55$$

Method 2: Multiply out first.

$$5(x + 4) = 55$$

$$5x + 20 = 55$$

subtract 20 $\quad 5x = 35$

divide by 5 $\quad \underline{x = 7}$

$$x \rightarrow \boxed{\times 5} \rightarrow \boxed{+ 20} \rightarrow 55$$
$$7 \leftarrow \boxed{\div 5} \leftarrow \boxed{- 20} \leftarrow 55$$

---

(1) Find the value of x in each of these equations.

   a $5(x + 4) = 65$ **b** $8(x - 2) = 72$

   c $10(x - 14) = 130$ **d** $7(x + 8) = 42$

(2) Find the value of x in each of these equations.

   a $\frac{1}{2}(x + 16) = 10$ **b** $\frac{1}{4}(x + 19) = 6$

   c $\frac{1}{5}(x - 2) = 2$ **d** $\frac{1}{3}(x + 5) = 2$

(3) Find the value of x in each of these equations.

   a $9(4x + 6) = 90$ **b** $2(5x + 1) = 72$

   c $5(8x - 15) = 45$ **d** $7(6x + 11) = 161$

(4) Find the value of x in each of these equations.

    a $4(x + 3) + 3(x + 7) = 61$ **b** $2(x + 9) + 6(x + 2) = 78$

    c $5(6x - 1) + 7(4x + 4) = 52$ **d** $2(3x + 9) + 4(x - 1) = 4$

TASK 6: Equations with x on both sides

◉ Points to remember

⊙ Look at any equation carefully before deciding what steps you need to take.

⊙ When you have x terms on both sides of the equation, collect them together on one side of the equation. Collect numbers together on the other side. Then simplify the equation.

⊙ Remember that whatever you do to one side of the equation you must do to the other side to keep the equation in balance.

(1) Find the value of x in each of these equations.

    a $8x + 3 = 6x + 5$ **b** $7x + 2 = 4x + 11$

    c $6x + 2 = 3x + 17$ **d** $10x - 2 = 7x + 4$

(2) Find the value of x in each of these equations.

    a $2x + 14 = 5x + 2$ **b** $5x + 6 = 7x + 4$

    c $3x + 1 = 4x - 5$ **d** $7x + 5 = 9x - 1$

(3) Find the value of x in each of these equations.

    a $9x + 7 = 27 - x$ **b** $3x - 5 = 30 - 2x$

    c $10x + 3 = 54 - 7x$ **d** $7x + 12 = 60 - 5x$

(4) Find the value of x in each of these equations.

    a $16 - 5x = 12 - x$ **b** $23 - 3x = 17 - 2x$

    c $7 - 8x = 6 - 6x$ **d** $7 - 5x = 3 - 7x$

Enquiry 2

TASK 1: Collecting continuous data

 Points to remember

⊙ **Continuous data** can be collected by measuring. The data can take any value within an interval. Examples are quantities such as length, weight, temperature, time and speed.

You will need some scrap paper and a stopwatch or a clock or watch with a second hand.

⊙ Ask three people to put this list of numbers in order of size from smallest to largest.

⊙ Time how long it takes them from first seeing the list to writing the correct order on some paper. Write the time in minutes and seconds.

The list of numbers:

7	12	5	15	8	2	6	14	19	11

TASK 2: Processing and representing continuous data

 Points to remember

In a **frequency diagram** for continuous data:

⊙ the bars touch because the data is continuous and so can take any value in the interval;

⊙ the horizontal axis is labelled as a scale.

Remember that, as with frequency diagrams for discrete data:

⊙ frequency always goes on the vertical axis;

⊙ the grid lines, not the spaces, are labelled on the vertical axis.

Example

Here are the times in seconds for three heats in a 400 m running race.

60.80 55.03 56.40 58.65 52.68 55.81 58.04 58.35
53.78 59.41 55.97 52.64 56.32 59.73 51.46 58.70
54.12 60.44 57.52 59.38 58.41 57.64 56.51 54.90

a Make a frequency table for the data.

b Draw a frequency diagram.

c What does the diagram show about the data?

a

Time (s)	Frequency
$50 \leqslant x < 52$	1
$52 \leqslant x < 54$	3
$54 \leqslant x < 56$	5
$56 \leqslant x < 58$	5
$58 \leqslant x < 60$	8
$60 \leqslant x < 62$	2

b

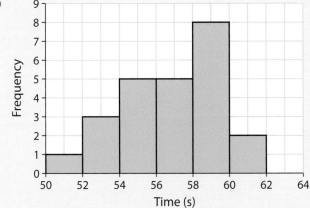

c The diagram shows that the majority of the times were between 54 and 60 seconds and that one person was faster than the rest.

You will need some graph paper.

1 This list gives the times in minutes and seconds for three heats of an 800 m running race. 2:23 means 2 minutes and 23 seconds.

2:23	2:25	2:20	2:16	2:21	2:20	2:34	2:29
2:24	2:28	2:24	2:12	2:17	2:23	2:30	2:13
2:19	2:23	2:25	2:23	2:16	2:14	2:25	2:24

a Copy and complete this frequency table for the data.

Time (min:s)	Frequency
$2:10 \leqslant x < 2:15$	
$2:15 \leqslant x < 2:20$	
$2:20 \leqslant x < 2:25$	
$2:25 \leqslant x < 2:30$	
$2:30 \leqslant x < 2:35$	

b Draw a frequency diagram to illustrate the data.
Use a scale of 2 cm to every 5 seconds on the horizontal axis from 2:00 minutes to 2:40 minutes.
Use a scale of 2 cm for every one person on the vertical axis.

2 In the long jump, 20 competitors jumped these distances in metres.

| 7.85 | 8.56 | 8.05 | 8.56 | 8.05 | 8.13 | 7.52 | 8.47 | 7.75 | 7.87 |
| 7.92 | 8.21 | 7.46 | 7.85 | 8.13 | 8.17 | 7.60 | 7.64 | 8.43 | 8.30 |

a Copy and complete this frequency table for the data.

Distance (m)	Frequency
$7.40 \leqslant x < 7.60$	
$7.60 \leqslant x < 7.80$	
$7.80 \leqslant x < 8.00$	
$8.00 \leqslant x < 8.20$	
$8.20 \leqslant x < 8.40$	
$8.40 \leqslant x < 8.60$	

b Draw a frequency diagram to illustrate the data.
Use a scale of 1 cm to every 0.1 m on the horizontal axis from 7.3 m to 8.8 m.
Use a scale of 2 cm for every one person on the vertical axis.

TASK 3: Analysing and interpreting distributions

 Points to remember

⊙ When you group data, choose class intervals that don't overlap.

⊙ When you draw a frequency diagram for continuous data:
- the bars should touch;
- label the horizontal axis as a scale;
- the frequency should go on the vertical axis;
- label the grid lines, not the spaces, on the vertical axis.

Example

The list shows the length of time 24 people waited at the checkout in a supermarket.
The times are in minutes and seconds. 2:19 means 2 minutes and 19 seconds.

2:19	2:05	3:04	2:12	1:02	2:30
4:01	2:42	3:09	2:55	3:44	4:09
0:30	1:43	2:08	2:13	3:31	4:25
1:18	3:17	2:37	2:24	3:55	4:46

a Draw a frequency table for the data.

The data is time so it is continuous.

Time (min:s)	Frequency
$0:00 \leqslant x < 1:00$	1
$1:00 \leqslant x < 2:00$	3
$2:00 \leqslant x < 3:00$	10
$3:00 \leqslant x < 4:00$	6
$4:00 \leqslant x < 5:00$	4

b Draw a frequency diagram for the data.

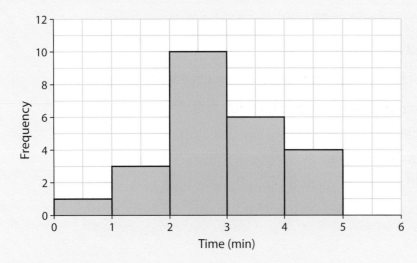

c What does the diagram show about the data?

The diagram shows that the modal group is between 2 and 3 minutes. Only one person waited less than one minute and four people waited between 4 and 5 minutes.

① The lengths of the tracks on two CD albums are shown in the table. The track lengths are in minutes and seconds.

Album 1	2:56	3:52	4:04	4:07	2:58	3:32	4:54	4:14	5:08	3:00	7:10	1:28
Album 2	3:36	3:22	3:56	3:32	3:35	3:46	3:58	3:57	3:59	4:32	0:30	6:48

a Put the data in a frequency table.

b For each album, draw a graph or diagram to illustrate the information.

c What are the similarities and differences between the lengths of the tracks on the two albums?

TASK 4: Communicating findings

 Points to remember

- Use a scatter graph to look for connections between two quantities.

- Put one quantity on the horizontal axis and the other quantity on the vertical axis. Draw both as a scale.

- Each point on the scatter graph represents a pair of values.

Example

This table shows the heights and foot lengths for 24 pupils.

Height (cm)	161	175	156	169	164	148	154	165	145	131	151	157
Foot (cm)	23	18	24	28	23	26	24	23.5	20	18	23	18
Height (cm)	160	159	176	188	156	166	159	172	172	151	171	175
Foot (cm)	22	29	27	27	28	35	20	26	22	20	26	27

Data source: www.censusatschool.ntu.ac.uk

Draw a scatter graph for the data. What does it show about the data?

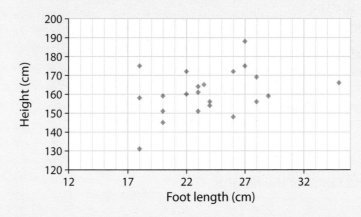

The scatter graph shows that there is some relationship between foot length and height. Generally people with longer feet are taller.

① This table shows the hand spans and wrist circumferences for 24 pupils.

Hand (cm)	19	19	18	20	20	20	13	21	18.2	21	15	15
Wrist (mm)	220	160	130	150	152	200	140	200	150	154	145	150
Hand (cm)	18	17	20.5	21	22	16	21	16	17	18	21	16
Wrist (mm)	135	145	155	170	160	110	180	200	150	140	155	120

Data source: www.censusatschool.ntu.ac.uk

a Draw a scatter graph to look for a relationship between hand span and wrist circumference.

b What does your graph show? Do people with a larger hand span generally have a bigger wrist measurement?

TASK 5: Mean, median and range

 Points to remember

The mode, median and mean are different ways of finding the average of a set of numbers. The range shows how much the numbers are spread out.

⊙ The **mode** is the number that occurs most often in the set.
⊙ To find the **mean**, add up all the numbers in the set and divide by the number of numbers in the set.
⊙ The **median** is the middle number, or the mean of the middle two numbers, when all the numbers in the set are arranged in order.
⊙ The **range** is the highest number in the set minus the lowest number.

Example

The heights of 10 people are 165, 155, 165, 145, 134, 140, 145, 154, 157 and 156 cm. Find the mean, median and range of the heights.

The mean:
$(165 + 155 + 165 + 145 + 134 + 140 + 145 + 154 + 157 + 156) ÷ 10 = 151.6$ cm

The median: Here are the numbers in order:

134, 140, 145, 145, (154, 155,) 156, 157, 165, 165.

The middle two numbers are 154 and 155, so the median is 154.5 cm.

The range: $165 - 134 = 31$ cm

You will need a calculator. Either use a copy of the class data collected earlier in this unit, or the data set on **S4.3 Resource sheet 3.1**.

(1) The five variables are:

- hand span
- foot length
- reaction time
- height
- standing jump distance

Pick three of the variables. For each one find the mean and the range.

(2) For one of the variables find the median.

(3) Why is it not sensible to find the mode with this type of data?

TASK 6: Comparing probabilities

Points to remember

- A **simulation** is a way of collecting data about a problem without having to carry out the actual experiment.

- A simulation is an easy-to-do experiment that behaves in the same way as the experiment we are unable to do.

You will need 1p, 2p and 5p coins.

You are going to use the coins to help you to choose what you are going to do on Saturday night. In this simulation the coins represent the following.

	1p	2p	5p
Head	Go out with friends	Eat popcorn	Dress up
Tail	Stay in to watch TV	Eat ice-cream	Dress casually

(1) a Flip the three coins. Write down the results.
What do they say you are going to do on Saturday night?

 b Flip the three coins 20 more times.
Make a table to show the results.

 c Which combination came up most often? What is its probability?

a Theoretically, how many different combinations are there?

b Did all these possibilities appear in your experiment? If not, why not?

TASK 7: Line graphs for time series

Points to remember

⊙ A line graph is useful for displaying continuous data against time.

⊙ Time always goes on the horizontal axis.

⊙ The other variable goes on the vertical axis.

⊙ Label the axes as scales.

Example

The table shows the maximum temperature in Belfast over 15 days in June 2006.

Day	1	2	3	4	5	6	7	8	9	10	11	12	13	14	15
Temp. (°C)	16	20	16	15	15	13	13	16	15	16	15	17	17	17	20

Data source: www.weatheronline.co.uk

Draw a line graph to show how the temperature changes over time.

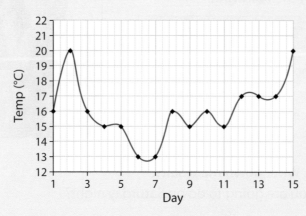

This table shows the maximum temperature in Winchester over the same 15 days.

Day	1	2	3	4	5	6	7	8	9	10	11	12	13	14	15
Temp. (°C)	23	23	22	17	19	18	18	18	22	17	14	17	20	22	24

① Use graph paper to draw a line graph to illustrate this data.

② Describe how the temperature changes over time in Winchester.

③ Compare the temperature in Belfast with the temperature in Winchester. You might find it helpful to draw the Belfast data on the same graph.

Constructions

TASK 1: Drawing arcs and circles

⊙ Points to remember

- ⊙ The **circumference** of a circle is the distance all the way round the edge of the circle.

- ⊙ The **radius** is the distance from the centre to the edge.

- ⊙ The **diameter** is the distance across the circle through the centre.

- ⊙ An **arc** is part of the circumference of a circle.

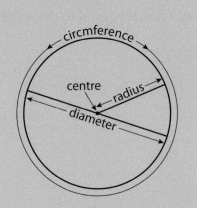

1. Measure the marked angles with a protractor.

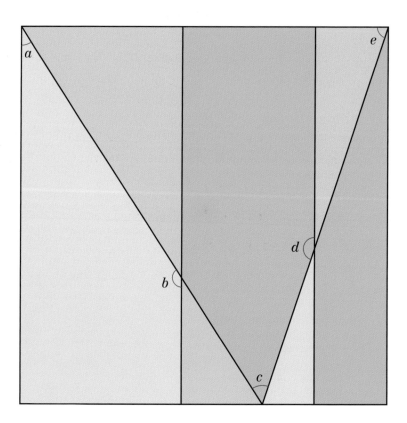

Draw a square of side length 16 centimetres.

Inside the square, construct four circles. The circles should touch each other and the sides of the square.

Leave any construction lines on your drawing.

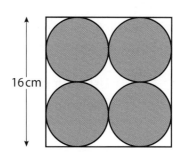

16 cm

TASK 2: Constructing midpoints and bisectors

⦿ Points to remember

Bisecting an angle

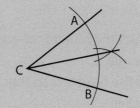

- ⦿ With the compass point at C, draw an arc crossing both arms at A and B.

- ⦿ With the compass point at A, draw an arc in the middle of the angle.

- ⦿ With the compass point at B, draw another arc in the middle of the angle to cross the first arc.

- ⦿ Draw the line from the C to the point where the two arcs cross.

- ⦿ This line is the **angle bisector**.

Constructing the midpoint and perpendicular bisector

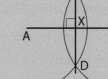

- ⦿ With centre A and radius more than half AB, draw an arc above and below AB.

- ⦿ With the same radius and with centre B, draw another arc to cut the first arc at C and D.

- ⦿ Join C and D to cut AB at X.

- ⦿ CD is the **perpendicular bisector** of AB.

- ⦿ X is the **midpoint** of the line AB.

You will need a ruler, protractor and compasses.
Show all your construction lines clearly.

1. Use your protractor to draw an angle of 135°.
   Use your compasses and ruler to bisect this angle.

2. Draw a line XY 9 cm long.
   Use your compasses and ruler to construct the perpendicular bisector and midpoint of XY.

3. Use your ruler to draw a triangle similar to this one.
   It does not need to be an exact copy but the base should be 8 cm long.
   Label the triangle PQR.

   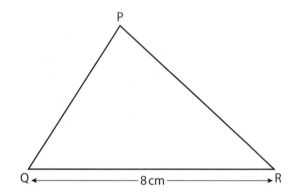

   Construct the bisector of each angle of the triangle.
   Extend the bisectors so that they cross each other.

   What do you notice?

TASK 3: Constructing triangles on paper

⊙ Points to remember

Constructing a triangle using SSS (side-side-side)

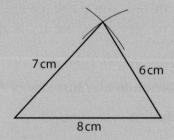

- ⊙ Draw a line segment the length of one of the sides of the triangle, leaving plenty of room above it.

- ⊙ Set the compasses to the length of one of the other sides. With the centre at one end of the line segment, draw an arc.

- ⊙ Set the compasses to the length of the third side. With the centre at the other end of the line segment, draw an arc to cross the first arc.

- ⊙ The third vertex of the triangle is where the two arcs cross. Join the ends of the line segment to the crossing point and label the triangle.

You will need a ruler, protractor, compasses and sharp pencil.
Show all your construction lines clearly.

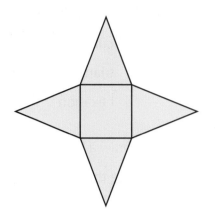

1 Draw accurately a net for a square-based pyramid. Use a protractor, compasses and a ruler to help.
Make the sides of the square 5 cm long and the sloping sides of the triangles 7 cm long.

2 All four faces of a rectangular tetrahedron are equilateral triangles.
Set your compasses to 6 cm. Use them to construct a net for a regular tetrahedron.
Leave in your construction lines.

TASK 4: Constructing triangles using ICT

Points to remember

⊙ In a **regular polygon**, all the sides are the same length and all the angles are equal.

⊙ The interior angles of a polygon add up to $180(n - 2)°$, where n is the number of sides. Use this formula to calculate the interior angle for a regular polygon.

Example

A pentagon has 5 sides, so $n = 5$.
The sum of the interior angles of a pentagon is
$180 \times (5 - 2) = 180 \times 3 = 540°$.

In a regular pentagon each interior angle will be $540 \div 5 = 108°$.

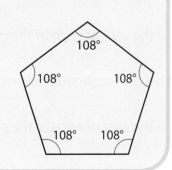

You will need a ruler, protractor and sharp pencil.

(1) Calculate the interior angle for each of these regular shapes.

a triangle   b quadrilateral   c pentagon

d hexagon   e heptagon   f octagon

(2) Draw a line segment 5 cm long in the middle of your page.

Use this line segment as one side of a regular octagon.
Use your ruler and protractor to construct the octagon.

TASK 5: Making shapes on pinboards

◉ Points to remember

⊙ You can find the area of a pinboard shape by dividing it into squares, rectangles and triangles, and thinking of triangles as halves.

⊙ These squares have areas of 1, 4 and 2 square units respectively.

You will need a ruler, sharp pencil and squared dotty paper.

A parallelogram has opposite sides equal and parallel.

Use dotty paper to investigate parallelograms **that are not squares or rectangles**. Parallelograms of the same shape and size but in different positions don't count as being 'different'.

(1) Using a 3 by 3 pinboard, how many different parallelograms can you make?

(2) What is the area of each of the parallelograms?

(3) Using a 4 by 4 pinboard, how many different parallelograms can you make?

(4) What is the area of each of the parallelograms?

TASK 6: Scale drawings

Points to remember

⊙ A **scale drawing** is a smaller drawing of an actual object.

⊙ The **scale** gives the relative size of the drawn length to the actual length. For example, a length of 1 cm on a plan representing a length of 20 m in a building is written as a scale of 1 cm : 20 m.

⊙ State the scale next to the drawing.

⊙ Corresponding measurements in the actual object and the scale drawing are all in the same ratio.

You will need a ruler, protractor and sharp pencil.

1. Write these scales as ratios in the form $1 : n$.

    a   2 cm to 10 m

    b   5 cm to 1 km

2. Tom has a plan of a new housing estate. The scale is 1 : 1000.

    a   The actual road through the estate is 600 m long. How long is the road on the plan?

    b   A house on the plan is 1.4 cm wide. How wide is the actual house?

3. A table tennis table is a rectangle 2.7 m long by 1.5 m wide.

    Using a scale of 1 : 10, make an accurate scale drawing of the table top.

    Use your scale drawing to work out the actual length of the diagonal of the table.

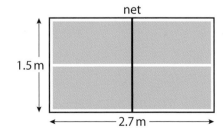

net

1.5 m

2.7 m

4 A hotel swimming pool is an L-shape.
   All the corners are right angles.

   Make an accurate scale drawing of the pool
   using a scale of 1 : 500.

   Use your scale drawing to work out the actual
   length of the distance AB.

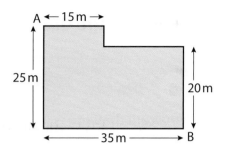

TASK 7: Using bearings

You will need a ruler, protractor and sharp pencil for this task.
You will also need a copy of **G4.4 Resource sheet 7.2**.

The resource sheet shows a **topograph**,
which tells you which direction places
are in and how far away they are.

Answer the questions on the
resource sheet.

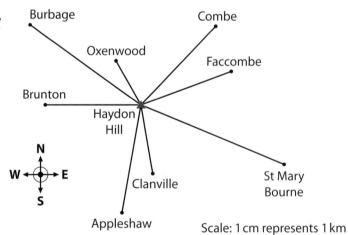

TASK 8: Exploring loci

 Points to remember

⊙ A locus is the set of points, or path, that follows a rule.

Examples

⊙ The locus of all the points 3 m from a point is a circle of radius 3 m.

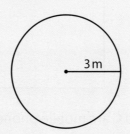

⊙ The locus of all the points equidistant from points A and B is the perpendicular bisector of the line segment AB.

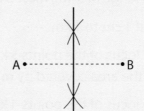

⊙ The locus of all the points equidistant from the two intersecting lines X and Y is the perpendicular bisector of the angle.

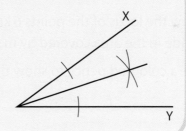

You will need a ruler, compasses and sharp pencil.

① Draw a triangle on your paper. Make each of the sides at least 6 cm long and leave plenty of space round the triangle. It can be any type of triangle.

Draw the locus of the points outside the triangle that are 2 cm from its perimeter.

(2) Copy this diagram in the middle of a piece of paper.
The copy does not need to be exact.

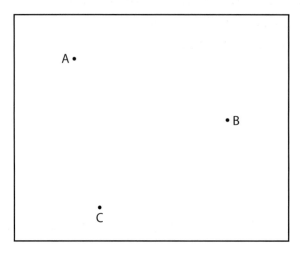

Points A, B and C are mobile phone masts.
Mast A has a range of 5 km, mast B has a range of 4 km and mast C has a range of 6 km.

Use a scale of 1 cm to 1 km.

a Draw the locus of the points 5 km from A.
Shade in the area covered by mast A.

b Draw the locus of the points 4 km from B.
Shade in the area covered by mast B.

c Draw the locus of the points 6 km from C.
Shade in the area covered by mast C.

d Use a coloured pencil to show the area covered by all three masts.

TASK 9: Using ICT to explore loci

Points to remember

○ You can use instructions, or rules, to describe the path of a moving point.

You will need a ruler, protractor and sharp pencil.

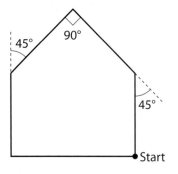

1 Copy and complete these instructions for drawing the house shape shown in the diagram. Assume you are at START and are facing up the page.

LT 90 FD 60
RT 90 FD 40
RT 45 FD 42
....
....
....

2 Write a set of instructions for drawing the house shape in question 1 double the size.

3 Make an accurate drawing of the shape given by this set of instructions.

FD 10 RT 90 FD 40 RT 90
FD 10 RT 90 FD 5 RT 90
FD 20 RT 90 FD 40 RT 90
FD 10 RT 90 FD 5 RT 90 FD 20

Using algebra

TASK 1: Simplifying expressions

 Points to remember

◉ You can simplify an algebraic expression by collecting together like terms. For example, expression $4x + 3x + 5 + 2x - 3$ can be simplified to $9x + 2$.

1 The expression in each cell is the result of adding the expressions in the two cells beneath it. Copy the diagrams and fill in the missing expressions.

a

```
          ┌─────────┐
          │    ?    │
     ┌─────────┬─────────┐
     │    ?    │    ?    │
┌─────────┬─────────┬─────────┐
│ 2a + b  │ 9a + 8b │  a − b  │
└─────────┴─────────┴─────────┘
```

b

```
               ┌─────────┐
               │    ?    │
          ┌─────────┬─────────┐
          │    ?    │    ?    │
     ┌─────────┬─────────┬─────────┐
     │ 5n + 2m │    ?    │ 6n + 2m │
┌─────────┬─────────┬─────────┬─────────┐
│    ?    │ 2n − m  │    ?    │ 3n + 2m │
└─────────┴─────────┴─────────┴─────────┘
```

2 Simplify these expressions by collecting together like terms.

a $7x + 5x + 3x + 4x$ **b** $5y + 2 + y + 3$

c $p + 7p + 2p + 9p + 8$ **d** $3q + 1 + q + 11$

e $4s + 3r + 7s - 2r$ **f** $t + 5t + 8t + 17$

g $1 + 6x + 2x + 9 - 3x$ **h** $8w + w + 1 + 3w - 5$

TASK 2: Factorising expressions

 Points to remember

⊙ The factors of a number are all the numbers that divide into it exactly.

⊙ When an algebraic expression contains brackets, you can multiply them out. For example: $5(2x + 4) = 10x + 20$

⊙ You can factorise an expression by finding the highest common factor (HCF) of each term. For example: $6x + 21 = 3(2x + 7)$

⊙ Factorising is the opposite to multiplying out brackets.

1　Find the matching pairs.

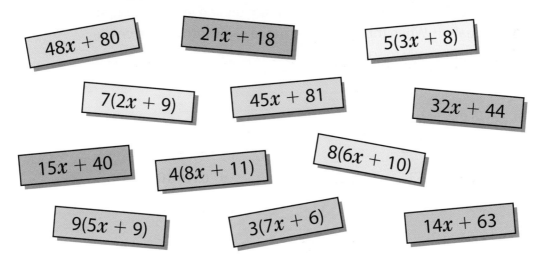

$48x + 80$　　$21x + 18$　　$5(3x + 8)$

$7(2x + 9)$　　$45x + 81$　　$32x + 44$

$15x + 40$　　$4(8x + 11)$　　$8(6x + 10)$

$9(5x + 9)$　　$3(7x + 6)$　　$14x + 63$

2　Factorise these expressions.

　　a　$12x + 20$　　　　　　　**b**　$14y + 35$

　　c　$40m - 55$　　　　　　　**d**　$18n + 21$

　　e　$10s + 14$　　　　　　　**f**　$30a - 48$

　　g　$16t - 40$　　　　　　　**h**　$33v + 77$

TASK 3: Solving linear equations

 Points to remember

- The equation $5x + 4 = 14$ has a unique solution.
- To solve the equation you can use the inverse function.

$$5x + 4 = 14 \qquad\qquad x \rightarrow \boxed{\times 5} \rightarrow \boxed{+4} \rightarrow 14$$

subtract 4 $\qquad 5x = 10 \qquad\qquad 2 \leftarrow \boxed{\div 5} \leftarrow \boxed{-4} \leftarrow 14$

add 5 $\qquad\quad \underline{x = 2}$

- What you do to one side of the equation you must do to the other to keep the equation in balance.

- Before solving a linear equation, first check whether you need to multiply out brackets or get all the terms containing letters to one side of the equation. When the equation is in the same form as the one above you are ready to solve it.

1 Solve these equations.

    a $5x + 13 = 43$ **b** $9x - 4 = 59$

    c $4x + 5 = 53$ **d** $6x + 10 = 4$

    e $8(x - 3) = 48$ **f** $5(x + 9) = 55$

    g $7(6x - 4) = 14$ **h** $8(5x + 6) = 248$

2 Solve these equations.

    a $6x + 5 = 4x + 7$ **b** $5x + 1 = x + 13$

    c $10x + 2 = 7x + 8$ **d** $7x - 3 = 5x + 5$

    e $3x + 1 = 21 - x$ **f** $5x - 30 = 26 - 3x$

    g $2x + 4 = 34 - 3x$ **h** $x + 5 = 21 - x$

TASK 4: Sketching linear graphs

 Points to remember

⊙ A sketch of a graph is a neat drawing using a pencil and ruler.

⊙ When you sketch a graph, look at the equation. Base your sketch on what you know about similar graphs.

⊙ The graph of $y = ax + b$ is a straight line. The gradient of the graph is a and the intercept of the y-axis is b.

Example

This is the graph of $y = x$. It is a straight line passing through the origin. It has a gradient of 1.

You can sketch the graph of $y = x + 3$ because you can see from its equation that it is parallel to $y = x$ and will cut the y-axis at (0, 3).

You can sketch the graph of $y = 3x$ because you can see from its equation that its gradient is 3 and it passes through the origin.

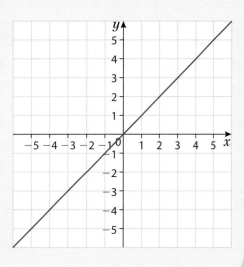

① Sketch the graphs of these equations. Use a new grid for each graph.

   a $y = x + 6$ **b** $y = x - 2$ **c** $y = x + 0.5$ **d** $y = x - 3$

   e $y = 2x$ **f** $y = 2x + 1$ **g** $y = -x$ **h** $y = -x - 2$

② Which of these equations have graphs parallel to $y = 3x$?

   a $y = x + 3$ **b** $y = 3x + 7$ **c** $y = -3x + 1$ **d** $y = 3x - 6$

③ Write down the equation of a graph parallel to $y = 7x$ that crosses the y-axis at the point (0, 4).

TASK 5: Drawing and interpreting linear graphs

⦿ **Points to remember**

⊙ To draw a straight-line graph accurately, plot three co-ordinate pairs.

⊙ A sketch of a graph is a neat drawing that shows some of the graph's features.

(1) You will need graph paper for this question.
Draw accurate graphs of these equations.
You can draw all the graphs on the same set of axes.

    a $y = 2x + 4$ **b** $y = 0.5x + 3$ **c** $y = 4x - 2$ **d** $y = -x + 1$

(2) Write down the equations of these linear graphs.

    a Gradient 3, intercept (0, 4)   **b** Gradient 2, intercept (0, 9)

    c Gradient 5, intercept (0, −6)   **d** Gradient 7, intercept (0, −8)

    e Gradient −1, intercept (0, −2)   **f** Gradient −3, intercept (0, −6)

TASK 6: Interpreting real-life graphs 2

⦿ **Points to remember**

⊙ When you draw or interpret graphs of real-life situations take care with the scales on the axes.

(1)

a Jim took 3 hours to drive his truck 117 miles.
What was his average speed?

b Mia walked 14 kilometres at an average speed of 4 kilometres per hour.
How long did her walk take?

c Olivia rode her bike 24 miles from Leeds to York.
Her journey took 2 hours 20 minutes, including a 20-minute stop for coffee.
What was her average speed?

② This is a graph to convert distances in miles to distances in kilometres.

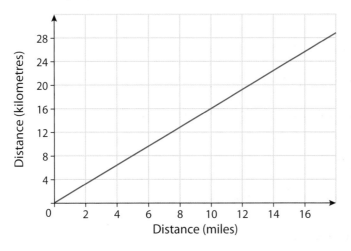

a   Use the graph to estimate the number of kilometres equivalent to 10 miles.

b   Use the graph to estimate the number of miles equivalent to 24 kilometres.

c   The distance from Calais to Blois is 528 kilometres.
     Use the graph to help you to estimate how many miles this is.

d   About how long will it take to drive from Calais to Blois at an average speed
     of 50 miles per hour, allowing for three hours of stops?

TASK 7: Word problems

● Points to remember

⊙ Read word problems carefully.

⊙ Define any letters you will use by saying, for example, 'Let x be…'.

⊙ Form an equation and solve it, showing your working.

⊙ Check that your answer fits the problem.

① I am thinking of a number. I double it and subtract 9. I get 85.
   What is my number?

② I am thinking of a number. I multiply it by 5 and add 9. I get 124.
   What is my number?

③ I am thinking of a number. I divide it by 6 and add 7. I get 16.
   What is my number?

(4) The sum of three consecutive whole numbers is 96.
What are the three numbers?

(5) The sum of five consecutive whole numbers is 60.
What are the five numbers?

(6) The result of multiplying a number by 7 and subtracting 9 is the same as multiplying the number by 6 and subtracting 2. What is the number?

(7) Natasha's sister is 17 and her uncle is 23. If you add half Natasha's age to that of her sister, then you get her uncle's age. How old is Natasha?

(8) Luke's computer game cost £15 more than William's. Lewis's computer game cost twice as much as Luke's. Altogether they spent £173. How much did each boy spend on their computer game?

TASK 8: Geometrical problems

Points to remember

⊙ Take time to read questions carefully.

⊙ Identify and define any letters you use.

⊙ Form an algebraic expression, equation or formula.

⊙ Set out each step of working.

⊙ Go back and make sure you have answered the original problem.

⊙ Check that your answers are sensible.

(1) The area of a rectangle is 64.5 cm². One side measures 7.5 cm.
What is the length of the other side?

(2) The area of a triangle is 31.5 cm². The base measures 7 cm.
What is its perpendicular height?

3   The perimeter of a regular octagon is 33.6 cm.
    What is the length of one of its sides?

4   In a rectangle the ratio length : width is 8 : 5.
    The perimeter of the rectangle is 78 cm.
    How long are the sides?

5   The sum of the lengths of the edges of a regular
    tetrahedron is 84 cm.
    What is the length of each edge?

Solving problems

TASK 1: Place value puzzles

 Points to remember

When you solve problems, remember to:

- be systematic;

- keep a careful record of your findings as you work;

- look for patterns in your findings and draw on these to come to some conclusions that you can explain and justify.

Take a set of 1–9 digit cards. For example, you could use playing cards or you could make nine squares of paper and write 1 to 9 on them.

$$\boxed{1}\ \boxed{2}\ \boxed{3}\ \boxed{4}\ \boxed{5}\ \boxed{6}\ \boxed{7}\ \boxed{8}\ \boxed{9}$$

Arrange all the cards, using as many + and − signs as you like, to make a calculation. Use each card once and only once.

For example, you could make a calculation with an answer of 104.

$$\boxed{1}\ \boxed{5}\ \boxed{9}\ +\ \boxed{6}\ \boxed{4}\ -\ \boxed{3}\ \boxed{2}\ -\ \boxed{8}\ \boxed{7}\ = 104$$

Make a calculation with an answer of 100. Write your calculation in your book.

TASK 2: Early history of numbers and counting

 Points to remember

⊙ You can often work out complex calculations by breaking them into simpler calculations.

⊙ When you calculate, try to choose the most efficient method.

 Did you know that...?

The Romans developed special symbols for some numbers. We still use these numerals on clocks, sundials, pages of books, chapter headings, and so on.

I	V	X	L	C	D
1	5	10	50	100	500

A smaller number to the right of a larger one means that it should be added. So VIII means 5 plus 3, or 8.

A smaller number to the left of a larger one means that it should be subtracted. So XL means 50 minus 10, or 40.

1 Convert these numbers to Roman numerals.

   a 27   **b** 156   **c** 89   **d** 2009

2 What numbers do these Roman numerals represent?

   a XLVIII   **b** CCXVII   **c** CDXX   **d** MMMX

3 Complete these calculations. Write your answer as a Roman numeral.

   a XVI + VII   **b** XVII − VI   **c** CXXI + CXII   **d** CXII × II

TASK 3: Missing digits and operations

 **Points to remember**

- Decide which information, given or needed, may be useful in solving the problem.
- Look for patterns and relationships in the information that you are given.
- Use your knowledge of number facts and place value to help to solve missing-digit or missing-operation problems.

Use your calculator to help you solve these problems.

1. In these problems, each ■ represents a missing digit.

   Work out what the missing digits are. Write the calculations in your book.

   a 3■ × ■9 = 1813

   b 323 × ■7 = 1518■

2. In these problems, each ● represents a missing operation.

   Work out what the missing operations are. Write the calculations in your book.

   a (2184 ● 91) ● 20 = 4

   b (148 ● 197) ● 15 = 23

3. Choose only from these numbers: 12, 36, 54, 75, 96.

   Work out which number goes in each box. Write the calculations in your book.

   a □ − (□ + □) = 6

   b (□ ÷ □) × □ = 432

   c (□ × □) − □ = 804

   d □ + (□ − □) = 93

Revision unit 1

TASK 1: Place value

 Points to remember

- To multiply a number by 10, 100 or 1000, move the digits one, two or three places to the left.
  To divide a number by 10, 100 or 1000, move the digits one, two or three places to the right.

- Multiplying by 0.1 is equivalent to multiplying by $\frac{1}{10}$ or dividing by 10.

- Multiplying by 0.01 is equivalent to multiplying by $\frac{1}{100}$ or dividing by 100.

- Dividing by 0.1 is equivalent to dividing by $\frac{1}{10}$ or multiplying by 10.

- Dividing by 0.01 is equivalent to dividing by $\frac{1}{100}$ or multiplying by 100.

 Level 4

Dylan has these number cards.

He made the number 4250 with his cards.

a Write the number that is 10 times as big as 4250.

b Write the number that is 1000 times as big as 4250.

c Write the number that is 4250 $\times$ 0.1.

d Write the number that is 4250 $\div$ 0.1.

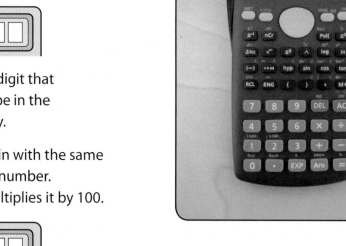

(2) *Level 4*

a Nicole puts a two-digit whole number into her calculator. She multiplies the number by 10.

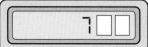

Write one other digit that you know must be in the calculator display.

b Nicole starts again with the same two-digit whole number.
This time she multiplies it by 100.

Write the four-digit number that must be in the calculator display.

(3) *Level 4*

Look at these number cards.

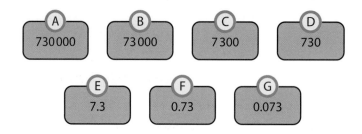

Write the letter of the card that is:

a ten times as big as 73

b one thousand times as big as 73

c one hundredth of 73

d the same as 73 × 0.1

e the same as 73 ÷ 0.01

TASK 2: Solving calculation problems

 Points to remember

When you solve problems:

⊙ read the question carefully;

⊙ write down the calculation that you need to do;

⊙ check that the answer is reasonable in the context of the question;

⊙ indicate your answer clearly, including units where appropriate.

You may **use a calculator** to answer questions 1 and 2.

 1   *2004 Progress Test level 4*

    a   The card shows the price of dinner at a restaurant.

> Dinner
> £14.95 each

      Twelve people had dinner. How much did they pay altogether?

    b   Another restaurant has different prices.

> Dinner
> adults £12.90 each
> children half price

      Two adults and their children had dinner.
      They paid £58.05 altogether.
      How many children had dinner?

2   *2005 level 5*

Two shops sell packs of pens.

Supermarket
Pack of 5 pens £6.25

Village shop
Pack of 6 pens £7.20

I want to buy 30 pens. In which shop are the pens cheaper?
You must show your working.

Do questions 3 and 4 **without using your calculator**. Remember to show your working.

(3) *Year 7 Optional Test level 4*

Tariq wants to use four planks of wood to make the top of a table.
Each plank of wood is 14 cm wide.
He wants the table to be 65 cm wide with equal spaces between the planks.

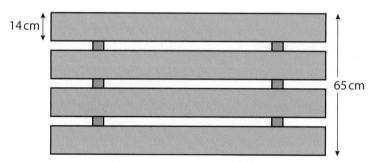

How much space should he leave between each of the planks of wood?
Show your working.

(4) *2003 level 5*

a I pay £16.20 to travel to work each week. I work for 45 weeks each year.
How much do I pay to travel to work each year?
Show your working.

b I could buy one season ticket that would let me travel for all 45 weeks.
It would cost £630. How much is that per week?

TASK 3: Expressions and sequences

 Points to remember

- A **term** is one or more numbers and/or letters combined by multiplication or division.

- **Like terms** have the same combination of letters. For example, $2a$ and $5a$ and a are all like terms.

- An **expression** is one or more terms combined by addition or subtraction.

- You can simplify an expression by collecting like terms.
  Example: $2x + x + 3x + 4 + 7 = 6x + 11$

- A **sequence** of numbers follows a pattern.
  You can find a rule to work out each term in a sequence.

1 *2000 level 5*

Write each expression in its simplest form.

a $7 + 2t + 3t$ **b** $b + 7 + 2b + 10$

c $(3d + 5) + (d - 2)$ **d** $3m - (-m)$

2 *1996 level 5*

Steve is making a series of patterns with black and grey square tiles.

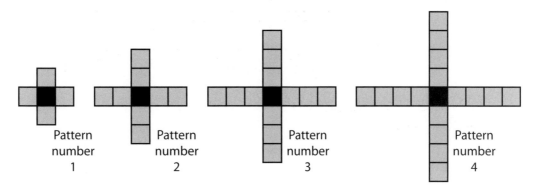

Pattern number 1   Pattern number 2   Pattern number 3   Pattern number 4

a Each pattern has 1 black tile at the centre.
Each new pattern has more grey tiles than the one before.
How many more grey tiles does Steve add each time he makes a new pattern?

b Steve says:

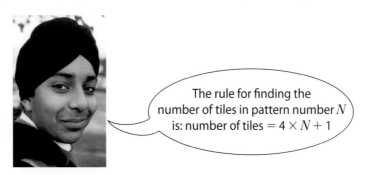

The rule for finding the number of tiles in pattern number N is: number of tiles $= 4 \times N + 1$

The 1 in Steve's rule represents the black tile.
What does the $4 \times N$ represent?

c Steve wants to make pattern number 15.
How many black tiles and how many grey tiles does he need?

d Steve uses 41 tiles altogether to make a pattern.
What is the number of the pattern he makes?

e Steve has 12 black tiles and 80 grey tiles.
What is the number of the biggest pattern Steve can make?

TASK 4: Perimeter, area and volume

 Points to remember

- Learn the formulae for the area of a rectangle, the area of a triangle, the area of a parallelogram and the volume of a cuboid:

  area of rectangle = base $\times$ height

  area of triangle = $\frac{1}{2} \times$ base $\times$ perpendicular height

  area of parallelogram = base $\times$ perpendicular height

  volume of cuboid = length $\times$ width $\times$ height
  $\qquad\qquad\qquad$ = area of base $\times$ height

- To find the area of a compound shape, divide it up with straight lines into rectangles and triangles.

- Triangles on the same base and with the same perpendicular height are equal in area.

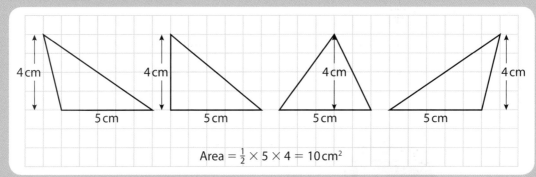

- Parallelograms on the same base and with the same perpendicular height are equal in area.

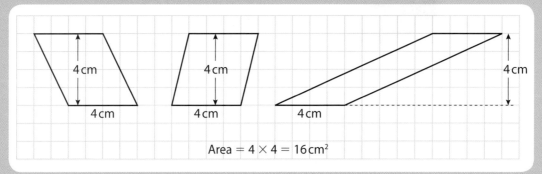

1. Copy and complete these sentences.

    a A new-born baby weighs about …
       0.3 kg   3 kg   30 kg   300 kg

    b A baby's bottle holds about …
       3 millilitres   300 millilitres   3 litres   300 litres

2. *Year 8 Optional Test level 4*

   The diagram shows a rectangle, drawn on centimetre squared paper.
   Copy the diagram on squared paper.

   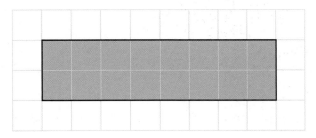

   On your squared paper:

   a draw a square that has the same area as the rectangle;

   b draw a square that has the same perimeter as the rectangle.

3. *Year 7 Optional Test level 5*

   Triangle ABC is drawn on centimetre squared paper.
   Copy the diagram on squared paper.

   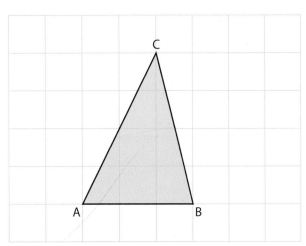

   On your squared paper, draw a rectangle that has the same area as triangle ABC.

1998 level 4

These cuboids are made from small cubes.
How many small cubes are there in each cuboid?

a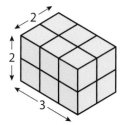

b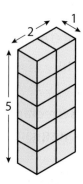

c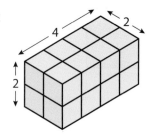

d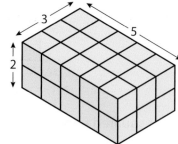

e This shape is made with two cuboids.
How many small cubes are there in
this shape?

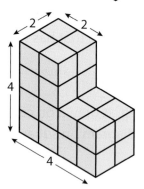

⑤ *Year 7 Optional Test level 6*

What is the area of this L-shape?

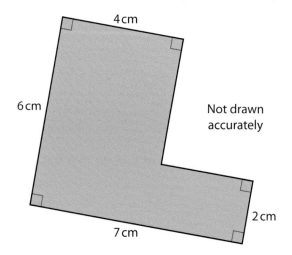

Not drawn
accurately

TASK 5: Probability

Points to remember

⊙ Probabilities are written as fractions, decimals or percentages.

⊙ The **theoretical probability** of an event is:

$$\frac{\text{number of successful outcomes}}{\text{total number of possible outcomes}}$$

⊙ The **experimental probability** of an event is:

$$\frac{\text{number of successful trials}}{\text{total number of trials}}$$

⊙ If p is the probability of an event happening, then the probability of the event not happening is $1 - p$.

⊙ Use a two-way table to show all the possible outcomes when two events occur at the same time or one after the other.

---

1 *2000 level 5*

A school has a new canteen.
A special person will be chosen to perform the opening ceremony.

The names of all the pupils, all the teachers and all the canteen staff are put in a box.
One name is taken out at random.
A pupil says:

> There are only three choices.
> It could be a pupil, a teacher or one of the canteen staff.
> The probability of it being a pupil is $\frac{1}{3}$.

The pupil is wrong. Explain why.

A machine gives out jelly beans in five colours: red, green, blue, yellow, black.
You cannot choose which colour you get.
There are the same number of each colour in the machine.

Two boys want a jelly bean each.

Oliver says: 'I don't like yellow ones or blue ones.'

Ryan says: 'I like all of them.'

a   What is the probability that Oliver will get a jelly bean that he likes?

b   What is the probability that Oliver will get a jelly bean that he does not like?

c   Copy the scale and draw an arrow
to show the probability that Oliver
will get a jelly bean that he likes.

d   What is the probability that Ryan will get a jelly bean that he likes?

e   Paige buys one jelly bean.
The arrow on this scale shows the probability that Paige gets a jelly bean
that she likes.

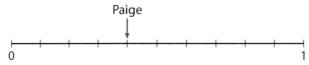

Write a sentence that could describe which jelly beans Paige likes.

3 *2001 level 5*

Mark and Kate each buy a family pack of crisps.
Each family pack contains ten bags of crisps.
The table shows how many bags of each flavour are in each family pack.

Flavour	Number of bags
plain	5
vinegar	2
chicken	2
cheese	1

a Mark is going to take a bag of crisps at random from his family pack.
Copy and complete these sentences.

The probability that the flavour will be .... is $\frac{1}{2}$.

The probability that the flavour will be cheese is ......

b Kate ate two bags of plain crisps from her family pack of ten bags.
Now she is going to take a bag at random from the bags that are left.
What is the probability that the flavour will be cheese?

c A shop sells 12 bags of crisps in a large pack.
I am going to take a bag at random from the large pack.
The probability of getting a bag of vinegar flavour is $\frac{1}{4}$.
How many bags of vinegar flavour crisps are in the large pack?

4 *2001 level 5*

A door has a security lock.
To open the door you must press the
correct buttons.

The code for the door is one letter followed
by a single-digit number, for example: B6.

a How many different codes are there altogether?
Show your working.

b I know that the correct code begins with D.
I press D. Then I guess the single-digit number.
What is the probability that I open the door?

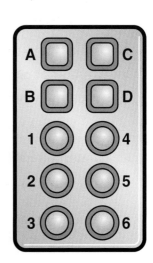

Revision unit 2

TASK 1: Percentages

 Points to remember

⊙ To find an amount after a **percentage discount**, subtract the percentage discount from 100%, then calculate this percentage of the original amount.

⊙ To find an amount after a **percentage increase**, add the percentage increase to 100%, then calculate this percentage of the original amount.

Example 1

Some ice skates at £78 are reduced by 4%.
What is the new price?

Take 4% from 100%, which leaves 96%.

Calculate 0.96 × 78 = 74.88.   **Answer: £74.88**

Example 2

The price of a £96 iPod increases by 8%.
What is its new price?

Add 8% to 100%, which gives 108%.

Calculate 1.08 × 96 = 103.68.   **Answer: £103.68**

① *2003 Progress Test level 4*

The pie chart shows information about children who go to a nursery school.

Altogether, 80 children go to the nursery school.

a   How many of the 80 children are two years old?

b   How many of the 80 children are four years old?

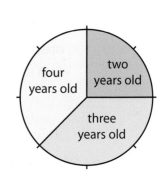

2 *1995 level 5*

a At a sports centre, people take part in one of five different sports.
This table shows the percentage of people who played badminton, football and squash on Friday.

Friday	
Badminton	10%
Football	40%
Squash	5%
Swimming	?
Tennis	?

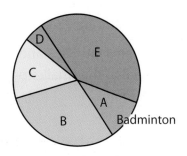

Which two sections of the pie chart show football and squash?
Badminton has been labelled for you.

b On Friday more people went swimming than played tennis.
Use the chart to estimate the percentage of people who went swimming.

c Use the chart to estimate the percentage of people who played tennis.
Make sure you have accounted for all the people.

d Altogether 260 people played the different sports on Friday.
Copy and complete this table to show how many people played badminton, football and squash on Friday.

Sport	Percentage	Number of people
Badminton	10%	26
Football	40%	...
Squash	5%	...

e Altogether, 260 people played the different sports on Friday and 700 people played the different sports on Saturday.

40% of the people played football on Friday,
but only 20% of the people played football on Saturday.

Mike said: '40% is more than 20%, so more people played football on Friday.'

Explain why Mike is wrong.

3 *Level 5*

Calculate:

a 8% of £26.50   **b** $12\frac{1}{2}$% of £98   **c** 105% of 90 kg

TASK 2: Ratio and proportion

 Points to remember

- If you are asked to divide a given quantity into two parts in the ratio 3 : 7, the two parts are $\frac{3}{10}$ and $\frac{7}{10}$ of the quantity.

- If you are given a ratio 2 : 7 and the size of the smaller part, find one share by dividing the smaller part by 2, then multiply by 7 to find the size of the larger part.

Here are some examples of ratio problems.

Example 1

Divide 40 cm into two parts in the ratio 2 : 3.

There are 2 + 3 = 5 shares.
1 share: 40 ÷ 5 = 8 cm
2 shares: 8 × 2 = 16 cm
3 shares: 8 × 3 = 24 cm
So the two parts are 16 cm and 24 cm.

Example 2

The ratio of the capacities of two jugs is 5 : 8.
The larger jug holds 400 ml. How much does the smaller jug hold?

400 ml is 8 shares.
1 share: 400 ÷ 8 = 50 ml
5 shares: 50 × 5 = 250 ml
So the smaller jug holds 250 ml.

Example 3

In a nursery school the ratio of boys to girls is 6 : 7.
There are 5 more girls than boys.
How many children are in the nursery school?

The difference between the two groups is 7 − 6 = 1 share.
5 children are 1 share.
There are 6 + 7 = 13 shares altogether.
So there are 13 shares, or 5 × 13 = 65 children, in the nursery school.

① *2005 level 5*

Work out the number of boys and girls in each class below.

a   In class 8M, there are 27 pupils.
    There are twice as many boys as girls.
    How many boys? How many girls?

b   In class 8K, there are 28 pupils.
    There are two more boys than girls.
    How many boys? How many girls?

c   In class 8T, there are 9 boys.
    The ratio of boys to girls is 1 : 2.
    How many boys? How many girls?

② *2002 level 5*

Screenwash is used to clean car windows.

To use Screenwash you mix it with water.

Winter mixture	**Summer mixture**
Mix **1** part Screenwash with **4** parts water.	Mix **1** part Screenwash with **9** parts water.

a   In winter, how much water should I mix with 150 ml of Screenwash?

b   In summer, how much Screenwash should I mix with 450 ml of water?

c   Is this statement correct?
    25% of winter mixture is Screenwash.
    Write **Yes** or **No**. Explain your answer.

③   The masses of two bags of sugar are in the ratio 2 : 5.
    The smaller bag of sugar has a mass of 300 g.
    What is the mass of the larger bag of sugar?

Extension problem

④   In 2007, Beechtown Football Club scored 18 more goals at home than away.
    The ratio of goals scored at home to goals scored away was 5 : 3.
    How many goals did the club score altogether at home and away?

TASK 3: Equations and graphs

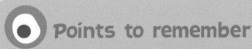 **Points to remember**

⊙ The linear equation $3x + 7 = 10$ has a unique solution, when $x = 1$.

⊙ The linear equation $3x + 2y = 10$ has an infinite number of solutions. The value of y depends on the value of x.

⊙ When you interpret linear graphs, work out the scales on the axes.

⊙ When a graph represents a real situation, think what it is about before trying to answer questions.

---

(1) *Year 7 level 4*

Complete question 1 on **R4.2 Resource sheet 3.2**.

(2) *2005 Practice Test level 4*

a Look at this equation.

$$x + y = 30$$

What could the values of x and y be? Write one pair of values.

b Now write a different pair of values that x and y could be.

c Here is a different equation.

$$a - b = 30$$

When $a = 40$, what is the value of b?

Class 9H were playing a number game.

Elin said:

Multiplying my number by 4 and then subtracting 5 gives the same answer as multiplying my number by 2 and then adding 1.

a Lena called Elin's number x and formed an equation:

$4x - 5 = 2x + 1$

Solve this equation and write down the value of x. Show your working.

Aled said:

Multiplying my number by 2 and then adding 5 gives the same answer as subtracting my number from 23.

b Call Aled's number y and write an equation.
Work out the value of Aled's number.

c Lena thought of two numbers which she called a and b.
She wrote down this information about them in the form of equations:

$a + 3b = 25$
$2a + b = 15$

Work out the values of a and b. Show your working.

TASK 4: Angles and transformations

Points to remember

⊙ When you identify equal angles in a geometric figure, always give your reasons.

⊙ Look out for vertically opposite angles, corresponding angles and alternate angles.

⊙ Also look out for angles on a straight line, in a triangle or around a point.

⊙ Reflection, rotation and translation leave the size and shape of the object unchanged.

⊙ Enlargement changes the size of the object but not its shape (i.e. angles).

You will need some squared paper.

1 *1999 level 5*

You can rotate triangle A onto triangle B.

a Copy the diagram on the right on squared paper.

Put a cross on the centre of rotation.

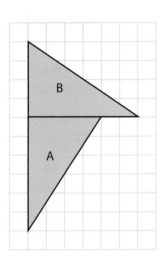

b The rotation is anticlockwise.
What is the angle of rotation?

c Copy the diagram below on squared paper.
Reflect triangle A in the mirror line.

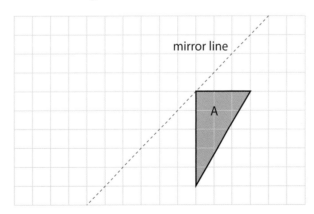

Emma has written a computer program to transform pictures of tiles. There are only two instructions in her program, 'reflect vertical' or 'rotate 90° clockwise'.

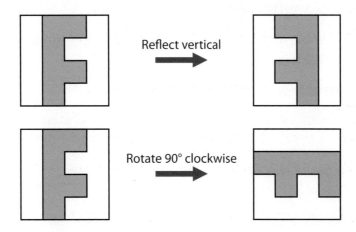

Emma wants to transform the first pattern to the second pattern.

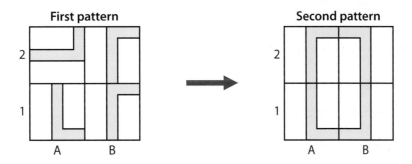

Tile A1 is in the correct position. Emma's instructions for tile A2 are:

A2 Reflect vertical, and then rotate 90° clockwise.

Copy and complete the instructions to transform the tiles B1 and B2.
You must use only 'reflect vertical' or 'rotate 90° clockwise'.

B1 Rotate 90° clockwise, and then ....

B2 ....

TASK 5: Representing and interpreting data

 Points to remember

⊙ In a pie chart the angle at the centre of the circle is proportional to the frequency for each category.

⊙ A pie chart shows only proportions not totals.

⊙ A two-way table allows two types of information to be presented and compared.

⊙ A line graph is a useful way of displaying continuous data against time.

⊙ Use the scales to read information from a graph as accurately as you can.

① *1997 level 5*

The Highway Code states the minimum distance there should be between cars.
There are different distances for bad weather and good weather.
The graph on the right shows this.

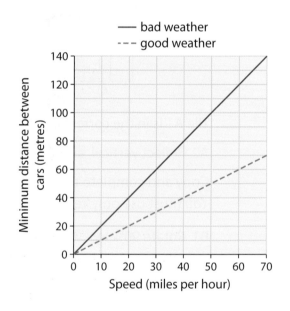

a The weather is bad. A car is travelling at 40 miles per hour. What is the minimum distance it should be from the car in front?

b The weather is good. A car is travelling at 55 miles per hour. What is the minimum distance it should be from the car in front?

c Mr Evans is driving 30 metres behind another car. The weather is bad. What is the maximum speed at which Mr Evans should be driving?

d Mrs Singh is driving at 50 miles per hour in good weather.
She is the minimum distance from the car in front.
It begins to rain heavily. Both cars slow down to 30 miles per hour.
Use the graph to work out how much Mrs Singh must increase her distance from the car in front.
Show how you worked it out.

These pie charts show some information about the ages of people in Greece and in Ireland.

There are about 10 million people in Greece, and there are about 3.5 million people in Ireland.

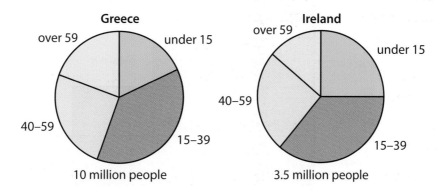

a Roughly what percentage of people in Greece are aged 40–59?

b There are about 10 million people in Greece.
Use your percentage from part **a** to work out roughly how many people in Greece are aged 40–59.

c Dewi says:

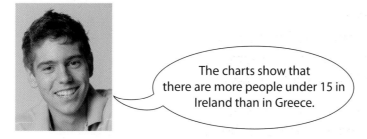

The charts show that there are more people under 15 in Ireland than in Greece.

Dewi is wrong. Explain why the charts do not show this.

d There are about 60 million people in the UK. The table shows roughly what percentage of people in the UK are of different ages.

under 15	15–39	40–59	over 59
20%	35%	25%	20%

Draw a pie chart to show the information in the table. Label each section of your pie chart clearly with the ages.

This table shows how much time it takes to fly between some cities.

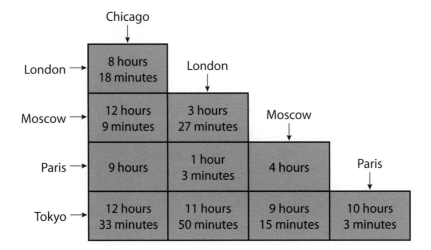

It takes 1 hour 3 minutes to fly from Paris to London.

a   How much time does it take to fly from Tokyo to Moscow?

b   Martin's flight leaves London at 07:00. What time will it be in London when Martin is due to land in Chicago?